ENDORSE

The love and courage that are at the heart of being human shine through this moving tale of a couple's journey with Alzheimer's. Cyndy discovers that her mindfulness practice is a valuable tool for navigating unfamiliar and unpredictable terrain which brings a heroic and life affirming dimension to caring for her husband. *Courageous Hearts* is a wonderful book for those who practice mindfulness as well as for anyone challenged by Alzheimer's.

—Anna Douglas, Ph.D.
One of the founding teachers of Spirit Rock

Courageous Hearts is a must read for anyone who is struggling to fix a disease that has no cure. Life will transform us. It's part of our soul's journey. *Courageous Hearts* gives us a peek as to how that process occurred in the lives of two people brought closer together because of dementia. Thank you Cyndy, for sharing your transformation with all of us.

—Kent Mathews, MSW, Lead Care Manager,
Family Caregiver Support Center
Pikes Peak Area Council of Governments
Area Agency on Aging

Courageous Hearts: A Journey through Alzheimer's is a powerful memoir of the truth of enduring love that meets and embraces pain with wisdom and an open heart. This book will be very helpful for caregivers who serve people living with memory loss.

—Bob Stahl, Ph.D. Co-author of *A Mindfulness-Based Stress Reduction Workbook* (1st & 2nd editions), *Living with Your Heart Wide Open, Calming the Rush of Panic, A Mindfulness-Based Stress Reduction Workbook for Anxiety,* and *MBSR Every Day.*

Where scientists and clinicians often focus solely on stress and coping related to the weighty tasks of caregiving, what Cyndy describes focuses the reader on the care partner's growth opportunities. This sad, funny, and engaging story of challenges, both big and small, invites us to stay mindful of our strengths, even in tragic circumstances.

—Sara Honn Qualls, Ph.D., ABPP
Director, Gerontology Center,
University of Colorado at Colorado Springs

Courageous Hearts is a powerful guidebook, in which Cyndy offers timeless wisdom for how difficult situations and perceived obstacles can lead to personal growth and insight. In doing that, she shares a deeply touching story about navigating her husband's Alzheimer's with mindfulness and compassion. I believe this book has a gem to offer everyone seeking more courage in meeting the unknown, as well as specific and direct encouragement for anyone in the role of caregiving or being with a loved one suffering from Alzheimer's.

—Deborah Eden Tull, Founder of Mindful Living Revolution
Author of *Relational Mindfulness: A Handbook for Deepening Our Relationship with Ourselves, Each Other, and Our Planet* (Wisdom, 2018).

In life there is change all around us, yet Alzheimer's disease seems to be a crash course in impermanence. Each person must find their own way as a caregiver. In *Courageous Hearts*, Cyndy shines a light on ways to make this journey clearer to traverse. Instead of reacting, she found ways to respond to what was occurring. Instead of hiding in fear, she found ways to summon her courage. Her honesty and vulnerability reach out to the reader and take their hand, helping them understand what is happening and giving them permission to feel their emotions and grieve. In doing so, their ability to be present is strengthened, which supports them in learning to let love to lead the way.

This book is a beacon whether you are at the beginning of this journey or recovering from it.

—Megan Carnarius RN NHA LMT, Author of *A Deeper Perspective on Alzheimer's and Other Dementias: Practical Tools with Spiritual Insights* (Findhorn Press, 2015).

Courageous HEARTS

A Journey Through Alzheimer's

CYNDY NOEL

An Imprint for GracePoint Publishing (www.GracePointPublishing.com)

GracePoint Matrix, LLC
624 S. Cascade Ave
Suite 201
Colorado Springs, CO 80903
www.GracePointMatrix.com
Email: Admin@GracePointMatrix.com
SAN # 991-6032

A Library of Congress Control Number has been requested and is pending.

ISBN: 978-1-955272-06-3
eISBN: 978-1-955272-05-6

Books may be purchased for educational, business, or sales promotional use. For bulk order requests and price schedule contact:
Orders@GracePointPublishing.com

Dedicated to those whose lives
have been touched by Alzheimer's Disease.

Foreword

As the director of Mindfulness Education at UCLA's Mindful Awareness Research Center, I have been immersed in mindfulness practice, research, and education since the 1990s.

I met Cyndy Noel when she participated in the Training in Mindfulness Facilitation at UCLA in 2015. This yearlong program trains facilitators to teach mindfulness to others. Participants come with a wide range of backgrounds, many working within the healthcare, education, mental health, or corporate spheres. Others come with personal visions—wanting to bring mindfulness to, for example, neglected children, refugees, underserved populations, or communities that dovetail with aspects of their lives.

I remember my initial meeting with Cyndy where she talked about her husband who had Alzheimer's, how mindfulness had significantly helped her care for her husband, and her vision to share mindfulness with others in her situation. It was a beautiful vision that I wholeheartedly endorsed. Little did I know that many years later it would become this wonderful book you are holding in your hands.

Over many decades I have observed mindfulness move from the margins to mainstream culture. While once a fringe practice in the West (although rooted in ancient meditative traditions of the East), it is now widely accepted as a helpful educational and clinical tool for stress reduction, pain management, emotional regulation, and the cultivation of positive mental states. Cyndy includes those aspects of mindfulness, in writing about the value it provided to her while she was caring for her husband.

The scientific literature and body of research around mindfulness is promising, but still very young. There is much to study, and we are likely just at the beginning of understanding the impact of mindfulness and how it relates to the wide-ranging situations that occur in life.

Periodically, I am asked, "Can mindfulness help with dementia, Alzheimer's, or cognitive decline?" The research in this area is limited, although promising. Studies have found that mindfulness may affect a broad range of measures in this population, including a reduction of cognitive decline, reduction in perceived stress, and an increase in quality of life, though there is a need for further research in this area, as well.

Perhaps more relevant here, mindfulness is helpful for the caregiver. Research has looked at the positive implications for those caring for people with Alzheimer's as well as caregiving for a variety of diseases and conditions. Those studies also point to reduction in perceived stress, improved quality of life, improved mood regulation, and, in these cases, a decrease in the care-burden. Again, the research is very young!

Beyond the science there is the human face of mindfulness—countless individuals using mindfulness where the rubber meets the road. This beautiful book is a testament to the experience and practice of mindfulness and offers another kind of validation.

Cyndy is a dedicated mindfulness practitioner who was faced with a huge challenge—the decline and ultimate loss of her beloved husband. As it is so clearly, authentically, and even humorously expressed in the book, she struggled significantly with the diagnosis. However, something began to shift when she remembered to apply her mindfulness practice. When she began to embrace the present moment, regulate her own emotions, and cultivate self-awareness and self-compassion, this tragedy moved to an extraordinary opportunity for learning and self-discovery.

As you will see, it deepened her relationship with her husband and herself. It is a lesson for all of us—no matter what we're facing. Our obstacles become our greatest teachers. Cyndy is a trustworthy guide, writing from deep in the trenches, to illuminate this.

Diana Winston, Director of Mindfulness Education

UCLA Mindful Awareness Research Center

Preface

Caring for Ron following his Alzheimer's diagnosis, taught me more than I could have imagined. As a result of being his care partner, I learned things about life that I had not been aware of in my previous sixty plus years.

Recently, on a soft, rainy Sunday morning, I settled comfortably into a chair in my bedroom and began reading from a book of poetry that I kept on the dresser, written by our friend, Robin Izer. She and Ron were in the same poetry group and even did a poetry reading together. She also read some of Ron's poems at his memorial service. Something about her book just being there on the dresser since his death, brings a sense of comfort to me.

As I read her poetry that morning, I was touched by her words. They helped me realize that in caring for Ron I had become stronger, more confident, and able to see "reality" from a new perspective, much broader than what I had known in the past.

The poem "Obstacles" was especially relevant, as in it Robin described how *the way is paved with obstacles* if we choose to perceive the events in our lives in that way.

or
we can
experience these
inevitable hurdles along the way
as high stepping stones
taken slowly
thoughtfully
building muscle
and will
toward a wider
vision of reality.

So, *Courageous Hearts* has come into being. It seems to have a life of its own. I was inspired to write how, as a result of my journey with Ron, I also learned the value of something else that Robin spoke of in the same work,

where we accept
what is
unconditionally.

"Spiral" is a poem I came upon later, in which she described,

learning to see
through the eyes
of the heart.

That is another one of the gifts that I received from Ron, and I would like to share my journey with you.

With deep gratitude to Robin Izer
for permission to use the poetry from her book,
Visions of New Being: Meditations & Poems.

Introduction

"It is so often the hard places that encourage us to grow and find the strengths, tenacity, and gifts we may have believed we never had."

Mark Coleman
From *Suffering to Peace: The True Promise of Mindfulness*

Most of us live in a manner in which we have normalized what occurs in our lives. "Normal" is generally a comfortable and familiar place, though trying to maintain that perspective may not always produce results that are beneficial to us and others especially when challenges occur.

I had the opportunity to discover that. When my husband, Ron, began having symptoms of memory loss, my life suddenly felt out of control. The normal life we had together seemed to be falling apart. I didn't know what to do. I had learned to be nice and do things right, but that was no longer working. I didn't even feel like being nice. This wasn't the man I married. Gradually, I began to see that he, too, was struggling.

We both wished that life would get back to normal. In fact, we had good skills for managing our lives and our marriage, or so we thought. But this was big. I wondered how he could be so thoughtless and inconsiderate of me. He wondered how I could be so angry and negative about him. We couldn't even talk about what was happening in the way that we had previously resolved issues.

As I became more aware of Ron's memory loss and how it was affecting our lives, I read a lot and reached out to professionals involved with issues related to seniors, as I began to see that his symptoms were similar to those of Alzheimer's disease. Since I had never known anyone who had that, understanding more about its progression and the behavioral issues that occurred throughout the disease was a steep learning curve.

I didn't like what I was learning; I was afraid and mad. I was also feeling sad due to the many losses that were involved the loss of a partner to help with managing our lives from day to day, the loss of the person with whom I shared the activities and conversations that were an important part of my life, the loss of the closeness and intimacy that we shared, and the perception that the personal growth that had been the basis for our relationship was no longer going to occur.

Thankfully, I was also learning about the resources that were available in the community to support us. One of those was the Alzheimer's Association. I attended many of their classes and eventually joined a support group in which I participated for the duration of our journey.

Having learned to do things myself, reaching out to others was a new experience. I soon came to appreciate the value of doing that.

As I learned more about the disease and processed the emotions associated with the many personal losses that were involved, I eventually committed to being Ron's care partner for the duration. The uncertainty associated with making that decision was huge. I learned that the journey ends when the person with Alzheimer's dies, and, of course, there's no telling when that will occur.

Though I had learned about the various stages of Alzheimer's, the physical and mental decline associated with each stage, and the behaviors one might expect, I quickly saw that those were just guidelines. Ron's behaviors did not really fit into any format. So much for my skills at managing a project.

Suddenly, as things felt more and more out of control, it became apparent that I needed to find a way to navigate the uncertainty that was occurring.

It was very challenging. At times I saw my inability to respond to what was happening in a helpful way due to being pulled off into my own emotional reactions.

I was reminded that Ron and I had practiced mindfulness, based on The Mindfulness-Based Stress Reduction (MBSR) program developed by Jon Kabat Zinn. There was no denying that this journey with Alzheimer's was stressful.

Thankfully, I began to find ways to incorporate mindfulness into what was occurring while I was with Ron. In doing that, I could see myself being less reactive and kinder to both of us. In fact, mindfulness even deepened my appreciation of some of the good times we shared, despite him having Alzheimer's.

One of the things that I learned in the classes I had been taking at the Alzheimer's Association was the importance of taking care of myself while caring for Ron. I began to see how valuable mindfulness was in helping me do that as well. When I felt myself being challenged by a situation, taking a deep breath and pausing helped me avoid reacting in an unhelpful way. When, on occasion, my emotions got the best of me, and I did react, I was able to have compassion and be kind to myself.

Ron's decline over the next eight years was filled with challenges, humor, sadness, and many experiences that I could never have imagined. I obtained help in order to be able to care for him at home which I did until he could no longer walk. He then lived in a skilled nursing facility that specialized in memory care for almost two years.

When the staff advised us that his death seemed imminent based on his symptoms, many of our family members came and gathered around his bed, sharing memories and love with him. His son and I were with him the next morning when he passed away, and the family soon returned to honor his passing and see him off.

In spite of being mad at the beginning of our journey, in the end I felt more love than I could have imagined. It was different from being "in love," as it had been earlier in our marriage. Instead, it was simply "being love." Along the way, I developed a deeper understanding and respect for the love and courage that are the essence of being human; for that I am grateful.

Note: I recognize that Alzheimer's plays out very differently with each individual and understand that the behavior of those with the disease and the situations for each caregiver can vary greatly. Having shared my story, I have the deepest regard for those whose journey may be more challenging. My hope is that some of my experiences can be used as a reminder or offer another way of being with a situation that will lessen the burden and bring more ease and understanding to those whose lives are impacted by Alzheimer's disease.

Prologue

It was a beautiful Sunday morning in mid-September. While I cleaned up the kitchen after breakfast, Ron was outside walking circles around the house. That was one of his favorite activities and he had worn a path in the lawn. He said he liked doing it because, "Nothing changes; it's always the same." He seemed to find security in the routine and that made sense. He was trying to deal with his world that changed so drastically in recent years.

Thankfully, the yard was entirely fenced and having learned that Alzheimer's patients sometimes wander, I secured it with padlocks on the front and back gates to make sure he couldn't get out.

The day before, we had participated in the annual Walk to End Alzheimer's with others whom I had met in my support group. Having taken the opportunity to solicit donations for the Alzheimer's Association from our friends and families, we gathered in a park and started the walk as a group after taking our picture together. This was a first-time experience for all of us.

The Walk consisted of following a wide path along a creek for about a mile, then turning around and walking back to the park. But our paces varied, and we soon became separated from the other couples. Ron didn't really understand what it was about, but having been a track star in high school, he sensed there was a finish line, and he was determined to get there.

As we walked his pace slowed down, but he kept going. By the time we got to the halfway point where we were to turn around and walk back, he was visibly exhausted.

Since many of the walkers were either those with Alzheimer's or their elderly spouses, the walk was staffed with volunteers driving golf carts to pick up folks and take them back to the park. I gladly accepted a ride when I saw how tired Ron was.

Having arrived at what he perceived to be the finish line made his day. He was clearly pleased with himself, so I was careful not to mention that we had only walked halfway. When we got back to the park, I didn't see any of our friends, so I got a hot dog for both of us then drove home.

The next morning, I was curious to know how it had gone for Maria and Doug who started The Walk with our group. Since Ron seemed to be occupied walking around the house, I decided to call Maria and chat for a few minutes. After we finished talking, I went out to check on Ron. I circled the house. No Ron. I reversed the direction and circled the house again but no Ron. The locks were still on the gates so I went in the house, thinking that he must have passed by when I was on the phone.

I went upstairs and looked in his study, the bedroom, and the bathroom. I called out his name. No Ron. I could feel myself beginning to panic, the "what ifs" racing through my mind. Maybe he climbed the fence. I walked across the street to the middle school where he often thought his friends waited for him to play football on Sunday mornings. In fact, I had taken him there one day after breakfast when he wanted to go look for them. I thought he might have gone there again, but I didn't see him.

I felt desperate. Where was he? What should I do? I decided to drive around the neighborhood. We lived in the center of town about a mile from the downtown area. There was nothing that would limit him from going in any direction, all of which were familiar to Ron. He often walked to various places from our house.

It soon crossed my mind that the more time I spent driving around with no idea where he was, the farther he could go. So, I decided to go home and call to report a "missing person." Within minutes after calling 911, a police officer arrived. After I explained what happened, she searched the house, looking in every closet.

I suppose we might have found him hiding, though I figured that search was because they probably get some cases where instead of missing, the person may have been tied up or killed and stashed away. Who knows?

The officer showed me how Ron could have gotten out the front gate even though I had a padlock on it. So much for that! She then asked for a picture of him. I grabbed the one sitting on my desk. She copied it and sent a bulletin to all the officers. Soon the neighborhood was swarming with police cars.

The officer told me I needed to stay home in case Ron showed up or someone called with information. The police also did a reverse 911 call which notified all the neighbors about the missing person. Soon I was getting calls and visits from friends and neighbors wanting to know what they could do. It was comforting to see so many people trying to help. I could feel myself starting to calm down a bit, understanding that I had evidently done all I could do.

Worst case, I thought at some point I'd get a call from the emergency room as Ron might have fallen or been found somewhere, confused, and dehydrated since it was a warm day. I was glad that I had gotten him a Medic Alert bracelet so he could be identified.

Meanwhile, I got busy cleaning house. I figured I may as well use my time productively since I couldn't leave. It was also a good distraction.

The officer returned periodically, checking the closets every time she came. That felt crazy but I stopped letting it bother me. I could see it was just one of the requirements the police had for working a case with a missing person.

Around 5:00 p.m., the doorbell rang, and it was the news team from a local television station with the officer, wondering if they could do a story for the evening news. Why not? I felt bedraggled but there was no time to make sure I looked good to be on TV. They invited me outside where they questioned me about Ron's disappearance. I provided as much information as I could about his behavior due to Alzheimer's.

I wanted Ron to be found. I remembered seeing other such stories on the local news and sometimes they didn't turn out well.

Just as we finished the interview, the officer got a call. She said they may have found him. She jumped in her car and took off. In the meantime, the TV reporter left. A little while later, another officer arrived with Ron in the backseat of his car. I breathed a sigh of relief.

He was found at a small, locally owned theater downtown where we occasionally went to see movies. After hearing the story, I shared it with Ron's son, Curt. He called the theater to get some more information but was unable to determine how long his dad had been there. He learned that Ron evidently raised some suspicion after ordering a bag of popcorn at the snack counter. When asked to pay, he pretended to reach into his back pocket and take out his billfold, unfolding invisible money and placing it in the hand of the person who was trying to collect. Obviously, that was unusual behavior. Thankfully, they called the police.

Since it was over six hours from the time he vanished, we wondered if Ron somehow intentionally went there or perhaps just came upon the theater while wandering around. I couldn't imagine that he left home thinking he was going to a movie and found his way there. Certainly, he couldn't pay for a movie since he didn't have his billfold. But at that theater they weren't strict about taking tickets as they generally are at the commercial theaters. It would have been easy enough to get in without a ticket. Perhaps he didn't raise any suspicion until the snack bar incident, as he had just been enjoying a movie—maybe repeatedly—all afternoon. We'll never know.

It was fascinating to see that Ron didn't act like anything was wrong when he got home. In fact, he told me how nice it was of the officer to give him a ride. He then sat down in his study to read and a few minutes later, asked me when dinner would be ready. It was just an ordinary day in his world.

The story was on TV that night and in the newspaper the next morning. The Alzheimer's Association got some good publicity, as they used it to segue into some educational pieces that they did on a local newscast throughout the week. It was timely as well, having occurred the day after the Walk to End Alzheimer's. Ron's Alzheimer's suddenly became highly visible in the community.

I was aware that my inability to keep him from wandering had evidently become public knowledge too. Oh well. My life was changing, as was Ron's.

I had gradually been learning about all that was involved in being Ron's care partner and was discovering that the role was full of new experiences, unlike anything I had previously known.

But it hadn't always been like that. Back when he was first showing symptoms, I felt confused too. Certainly, our marriage wasn't going as we had planned. In fact, I didn't even know if it would last. I was scared... and angry.

Chapter 1

I GREW UP IN THE 1950s when there was a right way and a wrong way—at least in our house. Like other females of that time, I was conditioned to be self-sacrificing and take care of a home and family. We learned to rely on a husband to provide financial support, make the big decisions, and manage the money.

That was back in the day when girls took Home Economics in junior high, and the boys took Shop. The roles were well-defined. A couple would spend years in those roles, raising a family and establishing themselves as upstanding citizens in the community; then the husband would retire, and they would live happily ever after.

For me, the TV show, *Leave It to Beaver*, depicted it perfectly, and Beaver's mother, June Cleaver, was my role model.

Ron, who was ten years older than I was, had a similar story. He had been raised with similar beliefs in which he would be the breadwinner and the dad.

He was the oldest of three boys, however, his situation had a twist. He had been conceived prior to his parents getting married, so he seemed to carry some emotional baggage related to feeling like he was not really wanted. In fact, he didn't recall his parents being there to nurse or cuddle him as an infant.

They were young and had other interests and plans, though they got married after discovering that his mother was pregnant. His dad had been hoping to attend college on a football scholarship, but he gave up on that and got a job instead.

It wasn't until Ron was old enough to participate in sports that he said he felt accepted by his family because sports were valued as an important male activity.

Throughout our lives, both Ron and I had been trying to play by the rules with which we were raised and living with the emotions we had not yet dealt with. We were questioning the reality of what we believed as children and young adults and tried out, unsuccessfully, in our first marriages.

We were on similar journeys, exploring life beyond the cultural conditioning and familial patterns we had learned. We were trying to understand who we were as individuals versus relying on meeting the expectations of others and defining ourselves with old patterns.

We were introduced by a couple who knew each of us. Ron had done birdwatching with Virginia through the local Audubon Society, and he was in a poetry group with her husband, Clark. They were the parents of Courtney who was my daughter, Aleah's, good friend. They saw a similarity in us, though Ron was ten years older than I was and his children, Curt, Tom, and Sara, were young adults when we met.

Ron was a published poet, though writing had not been part of his early adult life. Instead, his focus was on raising his children and supporting his family. But as a child he had been drawn to writing. In the poem he wrote, entitled "bio," he described himself as a young boy in school in Kansas:

in elementary school
there in that rural community
when the graphite of his number two pencil
wore to less than a nub (writing poems about flowers)
he was teased

Other than his grandma, Essie, most of his family and his peers had not been very accepting of a boy who wrote poems about flowers. So, to fit in, he turned to sports.

Ron thought he was going to become a teacher and coach when he graduated from the University of Nebraska, however, his girlfriend had another idea.

Since her father was a dentist, she and her family urged Ron to take a pre-dental exam. He was surprised by how well he scored on it. Realizing that he could make more money as a dentist than as a coach, he enrolled in dental school. Of course, the bonus of this decision was being accepted by his girlfriend and her family. It wasn't long before they got married.

However, he often told me that as he went through dental school, something seemed off. In his search for a life that would feel more authentic, Ron left Nebraska with his family after he graduated. As he described it in some prose, he left in response "to some inner understanding I couldn't explain." He went on to say,

> *When I left... I struggled to become someone other than a Nebraskan. Someone other than an all-American, other than a Christian. Perhaps it was my soul's rebelliousness and deep understanding, bigger than community, bigger than any belief system, bigger than winning or losing.*

I, too, was struggling. I had moved past the focus of being a wife and mother, as I had gotten a college degree and had a career in healthcare. I shocked myself the day I initiated a meeting at work due to issues that weren't being addressed with some of the clinics.

When my boss wanted to leave the meeting before they were resolved, I told him that he needed to stay until we got it fixed. Having been raised to fit in, typically I held myself back and wouldn't take the lead, especially when others, particularly men in higher positions, were present. After all, I had learned that women don't do that.

A message that seemed familiar from my childhood was, "Who do you think you are?"

After attending a vocational fair when I was in high school, I went home thinking I would like to be a social worker. But there was not much support in the culture, or in my family for a career of that type, so instead, I did secretarial work as a young woman. I learned to play by the rules and try to fit in, just as Ron had done.

Yet we felt stifled in those environments. We had each been in therapy in our attempts to discover a more authentic way of being. We were trying to heal events from our childhoods that we carried unconsciously into some of our earlier choices as adults.

Not only were we on similar journeys but our shared interests were confirmed when Ron and I discovered that we had many of the same books, including *Your Erroneous Zones,* and *Zen and the Art of Motorcycle Maintenance.* Our relationship felt like a good fit, so we decided to try marriage again. We envisioned exploring life in a new way and growing old together. In fact, Ron thought he had longevity in his genes as Grandma Essie had lived to be over one hundred.

We created our own wedding ceremony and acknowledged that our relationship was an "adventure" in which we would honor, comfort, listen to, and share life honestly with each other. In our vows, we said we would "love and cherish from this day forward," but we left out "for better or for worse, for richer or for poorer, in sickness and in health, 'til death do us part." We were going to make it up as we went along and not feel tied to those standard commitments. They hadn't worked the first time, anyway.

Instead, we shared the visions we had for our relationship with each other which included a poem Ron had written entitled "Whisper Dance." It had a line that spoke of dancing: "through the cracks in your armor," which was a good description of what we were each trying to do. One of our commitments was to review and renew our vows annually.

Nineteen years after our marriage in 1988, I was busy and involved in my career. My job as a Patient Representative at a local hospital was a salaried position which required long hours.

Ron had retired from dentistry early in our marriage then went back to school and became a part-time counselor. That seemed to fit as he occasionally struggled with depression based on his early childhood experiences. In addition to his counseling practice, he also worked as a substitute teacher and in a garden shop during the summers. He enjoyed the variety of work, and it supplemented his retirement income.

Since he was already a poet, it seemed only natural that, as he aged, Ron wanted to reach deeper and explore the creativity that lived inside him and had been dormant for so many years. So, when he was in his sixties, he began taking art classes. He was fascinated in developing his skill with various media and he created some very nice pieces.

He also began playing the fiddle. His interest in that was described in his poem, "marcellous and kin," where he expressed memories of his grandpa, Essie's husband:

> *standing there in bib overalls an ochre mustache*
> *toe tapping the bow whipping his arm*
> *fingers a blur over the fiddle strings – a hazy vision*
> *notes rolling off the walls*
> *of that small home against which stood*
> *those Kansas farmers rockin' back and forth*

Though in spite of taking lessons and practicing regularly, Ron's fiddling never seemed to improve.

At times, our relationship felt like our lives were going in two different directions. Ron was exploring his creativity while I was focused on my career. But it also seemed like something else was happening. In looking back at what we wrote when we reviewed and updated our commitments to each other in 2007, it was apparent that changes were occurring.

When describing his personal goals for the next five years, in addition to getting his poetry published and becoming good at playing the fiddle, Ron said he wanted to show me his "love and appreciation by doing things to help and by 'remembering.'" Interestingly, when we came to the question where we voiced a request of each other so our relationship could be more satisfying, I wrote, "Ron could do routine things without having to be reminded," and he noted that, "Cyndy could cease being so negative about me."

That November, one month after our anniversary, I removed my wedding ring. I was pissed. Ron was no longer the man I married. It was like he could not function in any way to which I could relate. That not only applied to our day-to-day household activities, but to our relationship—both emotionally and physically. We could no longer talk about things as we once did, and our attempts at making love were marginal at best. Evidently "happily ever after" was an expectation that lived somewhere deep inside of me, even though it wasn't in our vows.

Despite our intention to "dance" with whatever occurred during our marriage, there was a part of me that was ready to be done. It felt like my partner was gone. I was up against something that I could not understand and for which I had no patience. At times Ron appeared to be confused. I was confused too. I didn't understand what was happening to him and to our relationship. I felt alone.

Chapter 2

Looking back, I realized I had been dealing with a behavior of Ron's that I couldn't understand for quite some time. Ever since my benign brain tumor recurred in 2002, I could not hear out of my left ear.

I learned to adapt, as did my family, friends, and colleagues. They walked or sat on my right side so I could hear them when they spoke. However, Ron was raised in the era when walking on a sidewalk with a woman, gentlemen stayed on the side near the street so she wouldn't get splashed by passing traffic.

That summer he often accompanied me when I walked to work. Over and over, he would be on my left side, next to the street. I explained why we needed to trade places because I couldn't hear out of that ear, which we did... until the next time we walked. I tried to be patient yet wondered why it was so hard for him to remember that he always needed to be on my right side so I could hear him. Everybody else seemed to get that.

When we were walking, he also began to, very deliberately, avoid stepping on the cracks in the sidewalk. That slowed our pace, which was also frustrating to me. When I asked him why he was doing that he said, "Step on a crack, you'll break your mother's back."

I wondered, *Really?* This was a grown man and I had never heard him say anything like that before. In fact, I hadn't heard that since I was in grade school.

I noticed a few other things that seemed out of the ordinary for Ron, though I was able to explain them away. For instance, he did not remove the dead plants from the vegetable garden as he usually did in the fall. I just thought he had decided to do it differently. I'm not sure I even mentioned it to him.

He also quit watering the houseplants which he had done regularly during our marriage. Then, there was the night when he went out to go to his fiddle lesson and came home because he couldn't find the location. It was dark and in an unfamiliar part of town. I could imagine that even happening to me. And when we went somewhere together, I no longer felt comfortable with his driving. It seemed like he wasn't paying attention, so I always drove.

Around that same time, we went for an overnight visit to see some friends Ron had known since college. Glenda asked me what was wrong with Ron as she saw something quite different about him. After we got home, I noticed that Ron was corresponding with her via email. In response to the concerns she expressed, he wrote, "I think I have been dealing with depression my entire life and slowly, the coping mechanisms have been eliminated, leaving me with the need to deal directly with it."

Similarly, a member of his poetry group wrote an email to Ron in which she commented about how unusual it was for him not to get involved in the group critiques when they reviewed each other's poetry. She also referred to a conversation they had recently, in which Ron told her that he didn't really feel like he knew who he was anymore.

In response, Ron wrote:

> It is a difficult thing to communicate. I seem to have awakened to a past (my whole life) that troubles me. For whatever

reason, that evening I was perhaps more withdrawn and therefore appeared as I did. I'm just trying to stay with my process and, hopefully soon, it will pass.

We shared the same email address, so I was seeing his emails regularly. As the year went on, they revealed that Ron was constantly missing the meetings of the poetry group where he had been so valued. In another response, he again said it felt like he was losing all his "coping mechanisms."

As he usually did, especially once he became a counselor and had skills with which he could help others, Ron was trying to analyze himself and understand the reason for his own actions and change them. Based on how things had gone in the past, I thought he'd work it out and become his normal self again. Then, he would still be the Ron I knew, and we could get back on track with the life we had planned.

During that period, as a result of the things Ron was experiencing, we connected with the Aging Center that was associated with the local university. We learned that they did routine evaluations of cognitive function, so we scheduled him for one of those.

Following that, Ron wrote in his journal,

The memory testing I did today did NOT conclude any dementia or cognitive decline, however that leaves me with no answer as to what is going on with me.

He went on to write about how he would like to find ways to connect with me and his family better.

Clearly that test wasn't extensive enough to reveal the developing problem, as things seemed to be getting worse. I found myself becoming very angry when I would get home from a busy day at work to find dishes both from Ron's breakfast and lunch, spread around the kitchen.

How rude it seemed from my perspective. Especially since early in our relationship, based on Ron's suggestion, we had agreed not leave our dirty dishes, even in the sink. We were both very responsible about not leaving things for the other to do. However, now, not only was he going against his wishes, but he was making more for me to do. I had a hard time with that. I wanted a marriage in which I was valued and treated as an equal—not given more than my fair share.

He also quit loading the dishwasher after I made dinner, though on rare occasions he still unloaded it. When he did that, I often found things in unusual places. After having a big mess one morning when I was making a smoothie and discovered that the bottom piece of the blender was not screwed on right, I learned to check it every time I went to use it. I did not respond kindly out of my frustration and impatience when confronted by what appeared to be the result of Ron's lack of consideration. How could this man who had been so capable, now be so inept and insensitive?

He would often go to bed without telling me goodnight while I was working in my study. I wondered, *really?!* When he did that, I felt like I didn't matter to him. After commenting that he wanted to find ways to connect with me, that would have been a perfect way to do it. We always told each other goodnight if we went to bed sooner than the other. And though I brought it to his attention, nothing changed.

I came to refer to myself during that year and the period to come, as "the bitch!" I didn't like being that way. It was unlike me. It was just that I felt Ron was no longer capable of cooperating and respecting my needs and didn't seem to try or even care, so I reacted.

Since I was still working, I really needed his help and support at home, but it wasn't happening. I found myself feeling on my own more and more and was even beginning to feel uncertain about staying married to him. Yet, I also sensed that he was somehow not capable of being responsible for himself.

The following year Ron's behaviors changed some more. The things he was doing were causing consequences that were becoming more serious than just annoying me personally. Occasionally, I was able to see the situation from another perspective. At times, I was able to be less emotionally reactive. I was beginning to notice that his behaviors were having a direct impact on his own life, as well.

For instance, when I went to the dentist to have my teeth cleaned, they told me that Ron had not kept his appointment for replacing his temporary crown with the permanent one, nor had he called to cancel. Having been a dentist himself and a previous partner of Dr. Graton, he never would have done that. I knew something was wrong. I told them, "I'll see that he comes in even if I have to get off work and bring him myself."

When I talked to Ron about it, he told me he just forgot, and he went ahead and rescheduled the appointment. I made sure to keep track of it in my planner, reminding him on the day he was to go, and he got it taken care of without a further problem.

Then, there was the night he was at his poetry group, and I received a pre-collection call about one of his credit cards. We each maintained credit cards in our own names though we shared the household expenses. The caller explained that Ron's account had a balance of more than $1,000 and was overdue. Even the minimum had not been paid.

I provided information to make a payment from my checking account right then and there. I had a hard time understanding that. Even though I had excellent credit, early in our marriage Ron always reminded me to pay my credit cards in full every month and not to maintain a high balance. After that call, I went to his desk where I found amidst the piles, other credit card bills that were overdue or had a late charge on them. The Ron I knew would have been very embarrassed had he known that his account almost went to collection.

As a result of those incidents, I began to get involved in order to make sure he was taking care of things the way he would have wanted. When I stepped in, thankfully, he was usually cooperative. I created a spreadsheet so we could list all his outstanding balances and manage the payments on each of them until they were paid off.

I wondered why he was using so many credit cards in the first place, but it was too late for that conversation. I tried to explain the importance of reducing the number of credit cards that he used, and eventually I took all but one out of his billfold. Usually, we never interfered in each other's lives like that.

Every couple of weeks I would have him come into my study where I helped him write checks to pay his bills. I felt like a parent helping a child with a new activity. I did not yet understand that Ron's brain was unteachable. Finally, after doing that routine for a few months, I realized it was easier and less time-consuming to just pay his bills myself.

I asked Ron to put the mail on the dining room table when he brought it in so we could go through it together when I got home from work. Not only were his bills not getting paid, but some of my mail was getting lost on his desk. When, day after day, I came home and found that he had taken the mail to his desk, I really got mad. I found myself thinking, *After all the time I am devoting to help him straighten out his life, how could he do that and cause me more work?*

And I told him that... over and over. Having to track down the mail every day was clearly an inconvenience to me, and as a result the bitch showed up regularly since I was taking Ron's behaviors personally. It felt like he didn't respect or care about me anymore.

Eventually, I gave up on the idea of him putting the mail aside so we could go through it together and got a free-standing, locking mailbox. I kept the key. That was so contrary to the way Ron and I had shared our lives. I felt very sad about having to take such measures. It seemed like the Ron I knew was slipping further and further away.

One evening as I was leaving work at the hospital, I rode in the elevator with an older couple. I was trying to connect and be friendly, but the husband just stood there blankly staring at the floor. His wife was clearly uncomfortable and didn't seem to know what to do or say. As I got off at the first floor, I had the dreadful thought that that may be what was in store for me with Ron. Right after that I remember thinking, *that must be what Alzheimer's looks like.* I didn't want to go there! I tried to push it away, though at home in the evenings, I sometimes wondered if maybe Ron was getting dementia. I even Googled it a time or two. But no... that surely could not be what was happening.

In the meantime, Ron started to comment about how, when in a group conversation, he had trouble finding the right word to express what he was feeling. He was frustrated by that but attributed it to his tendency toward introversion and decided it was something he could fix if he just tried hard enough. It didn't seem impossible that this, too, was fixable. Surely there was a pill or a doctor or a book that would help.

He began to see Dr. Crandall, a geriatric psychiatrist he knew, due to what he was experiencing. Thankfully, he recognized it as something with which he needed help.

That was a period of struggle and soul-searching for me. I tiptoed onto the website for the Alzheimer's Association several times, but only as a curious outsider. There was no way I was going to let myself take that seriously.

I've since learned that denial is a common reaction that family members go through when confronted by the unexplainable behavior of a loved one with dementia. I guess I was no exception. In fact, I remembered that denial was one of the stages of grief that Elisabeth Kubler-Ross referred to in her classic book, *On Death and Dying*, which I had read years earlier. And anger was one of the stages too. Clearly, both those emotions related to what I was experiencing with the loss of Ron as I knew him, even though he was still very much a part of my life.

Ron's behavior was especially confusing to me the summer when his mother had a medical episode and ended up in the hospital, then in a skilled nursing facility. Given she was in her nineties and in poor health, I felt she might not live much longer, and it would be good for him to go see her. When I explained that this might be his last time to see her, he didn't appear to understand. That seemed strange after seeing how much he made sure to be involved during his dad's final days.

Finally, I decided to take some time off work and go to Nebraska with him so he could see her. I was putting way more energy into it than he was. Typically, we let each other make our own decisions about how to lead our lives.

She died later that summer, meaning another trip to attend the memorial service. But again, it didn't seem to register for Ron. Usually, we each packed our own clothes when preparing for a trip, but though I had been talking about leaving and was putting my things in the car, Ron just sat in his study. Eventually, I had to get some clothes together for him so we could go.

This time I drove and when we stopped for gas in Kearney, Nebraska, I was exhausted. So, I asked Ron if he could drive for a little while. As we left the gas station, I was looking in my travel bag for a snack and when I looked up, Ron had driven back onto the highway heading west instead of going east to Grand Island where he had grown up. After giving him instruction to turn around, I could see that I had to stay intensely involved and thought it would have been easier for me to have just kept driving.

That summer was a period of uncertainty and disappointment as Ron continued to unravel. He was losing interest in what was occurring and his skills for doing life were clearly suffering. My friends, coworkers, and Aleah heard much about my anger, frustration, and lack of patience with him.

I eventually began going to see Dr. Crandall with him. She said he might be showing symptoms of Alzheimer's and explained that long-term untreated depression could be a contributing factor. She tried having him take anti-depressants, as the test he had taken at the Aging Center noted that his difficulties could be related to depression and/or anxiety. However, she eventually terminated the medication due to side effects.

She also referred Ron to a neuropsychologist for a neuro-psych evaluation where he performed quite well on the test, with deficits in only a couple of areas. The neuropsychologist diagnosed him with "Minimal Cognitive Impairment," and said it "was not suggestive of full-blown dementia." However, she did recommend that Dr. Crandall also prescribe the two medications most often used for Alzheimer's: Aricept and Namenda.

I noticed that Ron was able to cover his forgetfulness quite well when he was in public at least for a while. That evidently also applied to his test-taking.

In fact, the neuropsychologist noted that he showed "good cognitive function in abstract reasoning and visual construction." I found it interesting, however, that he got a parking ticket while he was at her office because he forgot to put money in the meter.

In an email that he sent to his children to update them on what we were learning, Ron wrote:

> I am not admitting this publicly, but I do believe I'm in the early stages of Alzheimer's (there are lots of jokes about Alzheimer's, and I'm seeing now that it is no joke) and am looking for the best way to treat myself to alleviate that situation.

We both wished the situation could be "alleviated." Though he could clearly be quite lucid at times, it seemed like I was on my own to find our way in this crazy journey. Since he could not communicate with me, as we previously had done to resolve our issues, I had no way to understand what he was experiencing. I continued to feel very alone and became more and more estranged from him. I didn't even want him to touch me. He felt like a stranger.

Toward the end of that summer, one of my coworkers told me she had just received something in the mail that I might want to check out. When she gave the brochure to me, I saw that it was from the Alzheimer's Association. With that in my hand and a phone number to call right on the cover, a few minutes later I was at my desk calling their office in Denver.

They must hear from a lot of people like me. Who wants to call them!?! I still remember how kind and supportive the woman was. No telling what I said to her, but by the end of the call I felt like a huge burden had been lifted and there was help for what I was going through. She also gave me information about the local chapter of the Alzheimer's Association so I had somewhere I could go for support. That was a turning point—at least a small step on the journey that would last for the next eight years.

Within a few weeks, Curt accompanied me to the Alzheimer's Association for an orientation to learn about their services. In the meantime, I had also learned about the Area Agency on Aging, so we went there to find out about the services they offered.

Suddenly, though I had lived in the community for over forty years, I was discovering organizations that I never knew existed. Though I was just over sixty, my life seemed to be going in a direction that I had never imagined.

During the remainder of that year, I tried to come to terms with what was happening. I could see myself still wanting to hold onto my relationship with Ron as it had been. I remember, calling my friend, Maggie, who I had known for a very long time, and telling her about how things were changing as a result of his Alzheimer's. She later told me that in our conversation, I said, "I'm not sure I can handle this."

Chapter 3

I STARTED GOING TO THE Alzheimer's Association website to learn more. In reading about the disease, I learned that it couldn't be reversed or cured. No wonder Ron wasn't getting any better. But learning that and really understanding it were very different. I had a hard time getting my head around it.

I began to reach out a little bit more, trying to understand. A friend who was a social worker suggested that I get a copy of *Navigating the Alzheimer's Journey* by Carol Bowlby Sifton. She also thought it might be helpful if Curt and I went to visit an Alzheimer's Care Center, so we visited Namaste, a local care center that only accepted Alzheimer's patients. We couldn't imagine Ron ever living somewhere like that. He wasn't like those people.

I struggled with the part of me that wanted to get a plan. At least that might feel like I fixed it, for now. Yet I wasn't even clear where to begin. Thankfully, I seemed to be getting less reactive to Ron's behavior the more I got a sense that it was outside of his control and there was no way he could change it.

Due to my work schedule, it was hard to find time to go to the classes and support groups offered by the Alzheimer's Association, though looking back, I think that was just the excuse I used. I discovered that the Aging Center at the University of Colorado at Colorado Springs (UCCS), where Ron had gone for his initial testing, had a support group for caregivers so I joined. At least it didn't have the word *Alzheimer's* associated with it. The other participants had loved ones with various ailments and that group seemed to provide a less threatening way of easing myself into what was happening.

As time went on, Ron's behavior continued to present challenges. I was confused as, at times, he seemed normal. At least normal enough to trick my brain into thinking that nothing was wrong and that we could do life as we had always done. Like on the days when I walked to work, I would call him to come pick me up when I was ready to leave, and we would agree on a time to meet at the usual spot. But sometimes I would go out there and wait, and wait, and wait... finally realizing that he had already forgotten. At times I called to remind him from my cell phone, but other times it was just easier to walk home.

I felt angry, though I had quit taking it personally as I did early on. My perception was shifting from Ron not caring about my needs to seeing his behavior as an inconvenience and an aggravation.

On another occasion, he was going to start dinner so there wouldn't be much to do when I got home. That was like the old Ron and seemed simple enough. We talked about it while I was at work, and I asked him to put some potatoes in the oven to bake and prepare the broccoli so we could steam it while we grilled some chicken when I got home. However, he evidently turned the heat on under the pan with the broccoli at the same time he put the potatoes in the oven, then went upstairs to his study. When I got home the potatoes were done and the broccoli was black, as was the pan. Apparently even the smell of the burning broccoli had not registered with him. Though frustrated, I could see that he was trying to help, so I just did what was needed without adding comments from the bitch.

One day when I was at work, I got a call from the garden center where Ron worked part time, saying he came in, but it wasn't his day to work, and he wouldn't leave. They put him on the phone and finally I was able to convince him to go home. Luckily, that job was seasonal and was soon over. And thankfully, Mike and Gail, the owners of the center, had a personal experience with one of their parents who had Alzheimer's, so they understood. In fact, they suggested that I become familiar with what lay ahead and gave me their worn-out copy of *The 36-Hour Day* by Nancy Mace and Peter Rabins, a classic for folks caring for a loved one with Alzheimer's.

Several months later, Ron's behavior resulted in some major changes in our lives. The day before Thanksgiving, his son Tom was coming to town to make pumpkin pies with his dad. Before he arrived, Ron went to do a simple errand and return some books that he had recently borrowed from the library. I was at work and learned about this later when he called and amazingly was able to tell me what had happened.

Evidently, instead of going downtown to the library, he found himself driving east of the city just like we did when we went to Nebraska to visit his parents. Realizing that there was something wrong with that, he turned around and started heading to the house where he had lived with his first wife and their family. Again, he eventually realized that was not right and finally came upon a street that he recognized and became oriented enough to get home to our house.

After Tom arrived, he used Ron's car to take him to the library so they could return the books. During the short trip he noticed that the car was overheating so he stopped at a mechanic to have it checked. Evidently, when Ron was driving earlier, the temperature gauge had gone out but he didn't notice and continued to drive. That led to the car needing a new thermostat in addition to other repairs.

As a result of that event, I talked with Tom and Curt, and we agreed it was no longer safe for their dad to be driving. That had been a good wake up call. Thankfully, he didn't have an accident in the midst of his confusion, but we certainly didn't want to take that risk again.

They came over the day after Thanksgiving, and the three of us broke the news to Ron. Interestingly, there was not much response from him. I don't think he was able to understand exactly what it meant that he would no longer be able to drive. After Tom and Curt left, I simply found the car keys in Ron's drawer, hid them, and that was that. In the following days Ron would occasionally try to get in the car when it was parked on the driveway or if it was unlocked, he would get in and just sit there.

A few weeks later there was another incident. It was December and by mid-morning a big snowstorm had blown into town. I called home to check on Ron and there was no answer. I tried again a little later and still no answer. I had been transferred to a different location and was no longer working at the hospital nearby so I couldn't easily go home.

Instead, I called my neighbor, Kathryn, who had a key to the house and was familiar with what had been going on. I asked her if she would go check on Ron. She couldn't find him in the house, nor did she see footprints in the snow leaving the house. The car was still there, so he hadn't found the keys. That meant he was on foot and had been gone for a while. She checked a nearby restaurant where we thought he might have gone for lunch, but no Ron. With that news, I was starting to panic so I left work for the day. I called Curt and he met me at the house.

We were about to call the police to report that Ron was missing when there was a knock at the door. I answered and there stood Teryl, a good friend, with Ron by her side. He was only wearing a light jacket and was not dressed for what, by then, had become a blizzard.

When they came in, Teryl proceeded to tell us what happened. Curt and I listened in amazement. She said Ron had come to her door and asked if she could take him home. It seems that day he thought he needed to go to work at the School for the Blind, where he had been a substitute teacher. Since he didn't have a key to the car, he walked. It was probably a mile and a half from our house.

After hearing that, I called the school to see what happened. They said when Ron showed up, they told him they didn't need him, but he stayed. He told them, "Cyndy is coming to get me." After a while when I didn't come, he decided to walk home but by then it was snowing hard. We were all amazed and grateful that he found Teryl's house. It was only a few blocks away from the school, but we couldn't imagine that he actually knew where he was going. We wondered if maybe he just happened to be walking down her street and the house looked familiar to him. After thanking Teryl for her help, she left. We made Ron a bite to eat and helped him get warm and comfortable.

As the wind howled and the snow began to pile up, Curt and I realized that we were going to have to find someone to look after Ron while I was at work. Clearly, he could no longer be left alone. Since I wanted to work until I was sixty-five in order to maximize my retirement benefits and be eligible for Medicare, I would only be available to look after him on evenings and weekends for the next few years.

Not knowing what else to do, we called a home care agency and made arrangements for them to come over and meet with us when the storm subsided. We learned that the cost of full-time care from an agency would have been too much for our budget, so we decided to look at other options. Thankfully, it was a Friday, and we had a few days to figure it out before I had to go back to work.

Curt had been working from home and he thought that on some days he could probably come to our house and work while keeping an eye on his dad. Then I called Steve who had been helping us in the yard and had worked as a caregiver in the past. He said he could help too, and his charge was much less than the home care agency. So, we put together a schedule for the following week.

I then began to wonder how they could keep Ron occupied during the days. I thought maybe, due to his interest in art, he might like to draw or paint while Curt and Steve were watching him. We soon learned all that went into the set up and clean-up of his acrylics or watercolors was not worth the time, as Ron lost interest and didn't stay with the painting very long.

However, a friend who was an artist commented about how calming it was to move a pencil back and forth over paper. Hearing that, I went to a hobby store and got a sketch pad so that Ron could use the nice set of colored pencils which he had in his art supplies. That involved no preparation or clean up—and was always available as an option. Thankfully, he seemed to enjoy it and it was something that Steve and Curt could even do with him on occasion.

Having been with Ron during everything so far, I could see I was already managing his life and his care. Yet, I still struggled at times, feeling like I was under no obligation to stay and look after him. Our relationship was based on supporting each other to continue to step out of the limitations and behaviors we had taken on as children and young adults. There was no way Ron could support me now that he had Alzheimer's, and clearly, he was no longer able to be involved in his own process either.

In learning more about Alzheimer's, I understood that he would continue to lose his ability to function throughout the disease. His decline was already becoming very apparent.

I was hesitant. It felt like if I were to commit to staying with Ron, which was clearly going to be a journey of great uncertainty, I would likely lose my own momentum for personal growth and change. In fact, I had become aware that putting others ahead of me was a default pattern that I had taken on in my childhood. I talked to Curt and Tom. They were very kind and seemed to understand my dilemma. We were looking at options.

In the meantime, Dr. Crandall referred Ron for one more consultation in January the following year. This time it was to a neurologist. It seemed like it would carry more weight than the neuropsychologist or the screening he had received at the Aging Center, as this would be with a medical doctor.

Since he could no longer drive, I took Ron to the appointment and found it fascinating that he could perform so well when counting backward from one hundred by sevens or drawing a clock yet wasn't able to manage the rest of his life.

Like the previous evaluation that was done by the neuropsychologist, the neurologist, Dr. Aaron, felt that Ron had "Mild Cognitive Impairment." He also diagnosed Ron with "incoherent functional capabilities," that he said were primarily a result of untreated long-term depression. Dr. Aaron also said that Ron's deficits appeared to be more significant than they are due to an "affective depressive component," but that he had "well-retained higher cognitive functions." He told both of us that Ron needed to take a lot of walks, get the *New York Times* when he was out, read it thoroughly, then discuss it with someone.

As I drove us home, I found myself thinking that even if it was the local newspaper he picked up, Ron would probably get lost before he even got home. Yet, Dr. Aaron was trying to tell Ron that he needed to become more active and engaged in life.

I was perplexed as he also said there was a "fifty percent chance that Ron's symptoms could become dementia over the next four to five years." Something seemed off. Based on what I was learning, his symptoms were already demonstrating that he had dementia.

Yet, I simultaneously felt like maybe I had been having a bad dream and I would wake up to see that everything was fine. I was excited to tell his kids maybe it wasn't Alzheimer's. Maybe it could be fixed after all. But by the next day, my thoughts of it being more than "mild cognitive impairment" were confirmed.

Ron had always done the vacuuming as part of helping with our household chores, but that day, he couldn't even figure out how to turn it on or which tool to use.

We never saw Dr. Aaron again. Throughout the entire journey, I periodically saw evidence of Ron's "well-trained higher cognitive function" and in the earlier stages it was easy for those who didn't know him to be fooled. Evidently, even the doctors.

After talking with Dr. Crandall again and discussing what Dr. Aaron had suggested about treating the depression more aggressively, she reminded me that she had already tried anti-depressants. They may have been helpful many years prior, but by now we were seeing that what began with forgetfulness was progressing to a loss of intellectual and physical functioning. Ron's brain was clearly developing physiological changes that were irreparable. Those were called plaques and tangles.

I learned that amyloid plaques are clusters of protein that are found in the spaces between the nerve cells in the normal brain. With Alzheimer's, they clump together and disrupt communication between nerve cells and cause brain inflammation. Neurofibrillary tangles form inside of neurons and interfere with the cellular machinery used to create and recycle proteins, which ultimately kills the cell. Between the two, communication among the nerve cells is blocked, disrupting the processes that the cells need to function and survive. I was learning that it was this destruction and death of nerve cells that caused the symptoms that Ron was experiencing.

Having already come this far with Ron, as I learned more about the disease, I was beginning to see my interest in supporting him during his Alzheimer's journey. Little by little I seemed to be letting go of my thoughts about leaving the marriage. Yet at times, I could still sense my hesitation not only due to the impact I was imagining it would have on my own life, but because I also didn't feel like I knew what to do. Being a wife was something I felt confident about but being a care partner was different. The transition was not going to be easy.

Not only was I having a hard time letting go of Ron as I knew him but stepping into the unknown situations that were required of me was challenging.

I remember the time we went to spend the weekend with Tom and his family, who lived about two and a half hours away. They cooked a nice dinner, and we served our plates in the kitchen then carried them to the table in the dining area. I helped Ron with his plate first, then prepared my own.

As I approached the table to sit next to him and wait for the others to join us, he was already eating. The words spilled out of my mouth, reminding him that we needed to wait until everyone was seated before starting to eat. I sounded like a mom telling her child to practice good manners. It was taking me a while to understanding that our life had changed, and we were no longer "playing by the rules."

From what I was seeing, it was going to be a challenge to exert any influence over his behavior and there was clearly no way I was going to persuade him to act normal. I struggled to learn how to be with Ron, not understanding that I might never again feel like things were under control, and that "normal" was a product of my imagination.

Chapter 4

A FEW MONTHS LATER, ONE Sunday morning while making breakfast, I had an experience that really opened my eyes. Since weekday mornings tended to be hectic as I prepared to rush off to work, Sundays were about the only time Ron and I ate breakfast together throughout our entire marriage.

That morning, I was busy making hash browns and fried eggs. In the past, Ron would often help me. If not, he usually sat at the kitchen table, and we would chat. Often, he would glance through the newspaper at the same time, letting me know if he saw something interesting. But that day, while I was trying to prepare the eggs, he kept hovering over the stove and reaching across the area where I was working to get some hash browns out of the other skillet so he could snack on them. In doing that he was spilling them on the stovetop as well as getting in my way.

I asked him nicely if he would please sit down and told him I'd have his plate to him shortly, but he continued as if he didn't hear me.

Luckily, the bitch kept her mouth shut. I finished the eggs as best I could, then prepared his plate and helped him sit down to eat.

There I was again, even though I knew Ron had Alzheimer's, still trying hard to hold on to the life I had known and get him to be as he had always been. It was becoming very apparent that I needed to let go of my expectations and manage such occasions in a new way. I had trouble understanding that Ron was no longer able to change his behavior.

Suddenly, *I am the one who has to change,* flashed through my mind. It was more than just something I "knew." It felt like the words were carved into my being that morning. All at once I was seeing our situation from a whole new perspective.

I remembered the quote from Victor Frankl, "When we are no longer able to change a situation, we are challenged to change ourselves."

I guess I was going to have an opportunity to put that to the test. It was an enlightening moment to be sure and I was not enthused about my realization.

I became aware that, in order to be comfortable throughout my life, I had been seeing things in a limited way. I liked to feel that I had things organized and under control. It was easier to imagine that life would go as planned and it felt safer. However, Alzheimer's didn't fit neatly into the normalcy and predictability with which I had defined things by trying to look good and do it *right* all those years. Nor did it resonate with the beliefs of our culture where we are flooded with the expectation that we are to be happy and feel comfortable.

It seemed that Ron's Alzheimer's was giving me an opportunity to experience a whole new paradigm and question everything on which I had based my reality up until that time. Uncertainty was becoming the name of the game and I could see that it was going to be a slow and uncomfortable learning process.

Since he did not seem to behave in any predictable fashion, the ability for me to anticipate and prepare for what would happen next was impossible. Each day was new. I was beginning to see that I clearly had to find a way to let go of the stress of not knowing what was going to happen next.

About ten years prior to Ron beginning to show symptoms of Alzheimer's, he and I had taken classes with Jon Kabat-Zinn, Ph.D., who developed the Mindfulness-Based Stress Reduction (MBSR) Program at UMass Medical Center. In his programs, Kabat-Zinn explained how, in order to protect ourselves, humans have an alarm reaction that involves the release of stress hormones that enable us to fight, flee, or freeze when we feel threatened. That was how we survived back in the days when we lived in caves and our lives were often endangered.

I recognized that from my days of studying psychology, but in his book, *Full Catastrophe Living*, Kabat-Zinn further explains that nowadays, the source of our stress is not usually in the event itself, but in the way we perceive it. Though we're rarely in real physical danger, he says those same reactions can get triggered by "threats, real or imagined... to our sense of well-being or our desire to have things be a certain way."[1] That would certainly explain what was happening to me.

I never thought that Ron was going to harm me or endanger my safety, but, clearly, my comfort in being able to have things "be a certain way" was being threatened. Hence, when the bitch showed up, I was reacting with anger and frustration out of the stress and fear that I was experiencing. It was becoming clear that if I was going to change and commit to being his care partner, I needed to find ways to learn more about the disease and support myself in making the changes that were necessary.

I learned about an Early-Stage support group that was offered by the Alzheimer's Association, to which the "loved ones" were invited, as well. It was held once a month in the evening, which was doable since I was still working. I began attending and taking Ron along. The care partners met in one room and the "loved ones" met in another. I liked getting to know other spouses who were on the same journey, and it seemed good that Ron could get out and do something as well, especially in an environment where he was accepted and wasn't expected to act a certain way.

After attending for several months, I realized how lucky I was that Ron was generally calm and satisfied to draw rather than get into mischief around the house or be combative, as some of the other wives in the group were reporting. Some of their husbands had previously been engineers or mechanics. After getting Alzheimer's, they liked to tinker with things or take them apart—even appliances and furniture, and, of course, they didn't like to be interrupted in their work and redirected to something that was less damaging.

I was also able to leave work on occasion in order to take classes that were offered by the Alzheimer's Association during the day. Learning about the following early symptoms helped me understand the process that Ron had been going through.

1. Memory loss that disrupts daily life, such as forgetting appointments
2. Challenges in planning or solving problems, such as keeping track of bills.
3. Difficulty completing familiar tasks, like getting lost going somewhere.
4. Confusion with time or place, like not knowing where you live.
5. Trouble understanding visual images or spatial relationships, such as difficulty judging distances.
6. Problems with words in speaking or writing, such as trouble finding the right word.
7. Misplacing things and losing the ability to retrace steps.
8. Decreased or poor judgment, such as paying less attention to the needs of others.
9. Withdrawal from work and social activities.
10. Changes in mood and personality; becoming fearful and anxious. [2]

It was interesting to note how many of those I had seen in Ron the year that he was diagnosed. He forgot about his appointment at the dentist; wasn't paying his bills; got lost going to his fiddle class; and thought he still lived in the house where he had raised his children with his first wife.

When we were visiting his friends in Denver early on, he missed a step when going down some stairs and fell, evidently due to the issue regarding spatial relationships. He also complained about not being able to find words and wasn't telling me goodnight when he went to bed, nor was he helping with things as he had in the past.

In fact, the experience that Sunday morning when trying to cook breakfast, was a perfect example of him not paying attention to my needs.

He was right on track with many of the symptoms and though knowing that they were a part of the disease helped, I still had trouble adjusting to his new behaviors.

I also learned that there are three general stages in Alzheimer's— Early, Middle, and Late. Through the classes I was taking, I saw that while there are many characteristics and behaviors associated with certain stages of Alzheimer's, they are expressed in different ways and at different times by everyone. The stages were just guidelines that varied by each person and situation.

Clearly, Ron had many of the symptoms of the Early Stage during the first couple of years when something seemed a little off. It was during that period that I was in denial and had not wanted to pay attention to what I was seeing in him and he was trying to figure out what was wrong.

The classes also helped me understand that since there was no way to fix it, death was the way it ended, either directly as a result of the Alzheimer's or due to a comorbidity, such as heart disease. I learned that the average length of time that a person lives with Alzheimer's was eight to ten years and it could sometimes be a lot longer, especially for those who were healthy.

By the time I was beginning to understand more about the disease, it seemed like Ron was well into the Middle Stage. I learned that being confused as to where they are and having an increased tendency to wander was one of the symptoms that often shows up during that stage.

Ron provided an example of that one night at the end of the support group when we were all enjoying refreshments and visiting before we left. Typically, one of the facilitators stood by the door but she had evidently gotten sidetracked that night. When I was ready to leave, I couldn't find Ron and suddenly I felt panicked. Where was he?

I checked the restroom. He wasn't there. I told the others and we agreed after quickly scanning the area both inside and out, that he had probably left on his own. Beth was helping her husband get in the car to leave and said she would keep an eye out for Ron as they drove down the street. I decided to stay at the meeting hall for a few more minutes, in case he showed up.

Soon Beth and her husband returned with Ron in the backseat. He was just walking home. No big deal to him, though I doubt he would have found his way, especially at night. And besides, he would have had to cross four very busy streets to get to our house.

The experience that evening confirmed one of the things I was learning about Alzheimer's. I never knew what was going to happen next. Interestingly, it was also a harbinger of the event that happened later that year when Ron got out of the yard and went to the movies, even though I thought I had taken the necessary precautions to keep him from wandering.

As the months went on, I saw that as much as I wanted to hold onto the way life had been, those days were over. Ron, as I had known him, was gone, but instead of feeling the loss, the bitch showed up. I got scared, angry, and tried to find something to hold onto that was familiar. In learning more about the disease and hearing the stories of others in the support group, I was beginning to see the extent to which being the one who had to change, required me finding a way to come to terms with this crazy new life.

As my old version of reality kept falling apart, I was reminded again about the reason Ron and I had gotten married. We were going to support each other in letting go of the conditioning and habits we had developed over our lifetimes so we could become more authentically ourselves.

How ironic to think that it might be playing out in this way. This experience was causing me to come face to face with the beliefs and behaviors that I had previously used to manage my life. In fact, seeing that this experience might be an opportunity to change was confirmed when I later learned how experiences that bring about abrupt changes and shifts in our perspective can be of value, as they often serve to sever the ties that bind us to that with which we are familiar.

I wondered, if it had to come to this to get me to let go enough to change? I was curious. Then came the event that really sealed the deal for me in committing to care for Ron during his journey with Alzheimer's.

My friend Jeanne and I had known each other since long before I met Ron. In fact, we met during my first marriage, even before Aleah was born. We went way back. One of the things we shared was an interest in spirituality that we experienced in a realm outside of the Jewish and Methodist religions in which we had been raised. So, it seemed perfectly fitting that she invited me to join her one night for an event in which a woman was going to be playing crystal bowls. It was Jeanne's gift to me for my birthday.

I arranged for Curt to come spend the evening with his dad so I could attend. I took my meditation cushion as I understood it would be a somewhat meditative experience, though I didn't know exactly what to expect. After we arrived and got settled, I saw many other friends there, as well.

The woman who was playing the bowls was sitting on the floor, surrounded by them. She began tapping them softly with a heavy, padded stick. The sound of the vibrating bowls, each one emitting a different tone, filled the room. She explained that the sounds of the vibrating bowls create the perfect state for deep meditation, creative thinking, and intuitive messages. I began to feel myself relaxing even more.

Then suddenly, the peace and relaxation I was experiencing turned into sobs coming from somewhere deep inside me. I didn't want to bother the others, yet it felt important that I feel what was arising, so I cried as quietly as I could.

During that time, I felt like I was having a dream in which I became aware that if I were to continue my life without Ron, I would miss the opportunity to complete the healing we had set out to do. On the other hand, staying with him would require that I give up thinking I could change it or fix it and would involve learning to be with what was happening in whatever way supported him and myself. It gave me a new framework in which to hold it all. The experience touched me deeply and there was no questioning it.

That night I developed a clear commitment to do my best to care for Ron for the duration of his disease... and his life. It seemed that the intention we had established to use our relationship to explore our lives beyond the cultural norms, was playing out in a way that we could not have imagined. What if I could continue with my own journey to grow and change and, at the same time, care for Ron? I wondered, *what about him?* I was curious what might be happening in his "altered state."

After I fully committed myself to being Ron's care partner, I thought, how wonderful if this could be a journey of discovery and adventure rather than seeing it as a burden, as I had been doing. It was up to me to choose how to respond.

From what I was learning, I could see that knowing about the details of the disease and understanding how to care for a loved one who had Alzheimer's, was important. At the same time, choosing how I would perceive it was going to be important as well. It would have an impact on my role as Ron's care partner and on my own life, in the years that followed. But I still had a long way to go to step into this unfamiliar role.

Chapter 5

SEVERAL MONTHS AFTER THE MOMENT of insight in the kitchen that Sunday morning, I realized I had been neglecting my mindfulness practice. Due to all that had been happening over the last several years I was scrambling just to get through each day in order to stay on top of managing our lives. When I reacted to Ron and his unsettling behaviors as the bitch, I began to see it was because I was longing for the comfort of knowing that things were going to be familiar or at least predictable, and that was no longer possible.

Then I read something by Phillip Moffitt that clarified what I had been going through. He said, "When confronted with a difficult experience, the untrained mind wants to be anywhere but in the present moment, where it perceives acute unpleasantness. The mind becomes anxious whenever it's uncertain and reacts as if your survival is at stake." He went on to say, "Rather than staying with the experience and determining the best possible way to relate to it, the mind jumps to creating a story that involves worrying about the future or judging oneself or others based on past experiences."[1] That was a perfect explanation for what I had been doing and was another way of seeing what Jon Kabat-Zinn said about the way we react in times of stress.

It was stressful when things didn't go as I expected and I didn't know what to do, nor how it was going to affect our lives in the future. I wondered how I would ever be able to see it from another perspective and perhaps even be kind and genuine in my interactions with Ron, as we had been with each other prior to him having Alzheimer's. My focus had certainly not been on bringing awareness to the uncomfortable feelings I was experiencing, even though that is one of the fundamental components of mindfulness.

In their book, *Fully Present: The Science, Art, and Practice of Mindfulness,* Susan Smalley, Ph.D. and Diana Winston define mindfulness as "the art of observing your physical, emotional, and mental experiences with deliberate, open, and curious attention."[2] Jon Kabat-Zinn always included the importance of being non-judgmental as well.

Smalley and Winston go on to explain that though mindfulness is typically "cultivated through a daily formal meditation practice," you can also use it by "remembering to be aware of your present-moment experience anytime in the course of a day."[3] I could see that I was going to have many opportunities to practice paying attention.

I noticed that when the bitch interacted with Ron by being short, complaining about what he was doing, or blaming him for something, it did not serve any purpose other than to invalidate him, cause me to feel either guilty or like a victim of the circumstances, and make the entire situation worse for both of us. It was becoming clear that in this situation, I was going to have many chances to let go of what was familiar to me.

How was I going to achieve my previous way of playing by the rules when I couldn't even understand what the rules were?

I was learning that there were few absolutes in caring for one with Alzheimer's, aside from being respectful and keeping the person safe and comfortable. Of course, there were many specific skills within that paradigm, with which I became familiar, as the disease progressed.

At the same time, I was learning about the importance of taking care of myself so I could be there for Ron. That too, was not something with which I was very familiar, having always tended to put others first.

It seemed if I could be with what was occurring with openness and curiosity, it would be easier than trying to get a plan and do it right. Perhaps it would even reduce the stress of struggling with the things that were occurring.

Kabat-Zinn spoke of this in his book when he said, "As soon as you bring awareness to what is going on in a stressful situation, you have already changed that situation dramatically."[4] Whew, maybe it would get easier but knowing what I knew about mindfulness, it certainly wasn't going to happen overnight; it would take time.

Then I came across something that really helped me soften my grip on trying to hold on to life as it had been. In *Full Catastrophe Living*, where Kabat-Zinn talked about stress reactivity, he referred to stressors that affect us over extended periods of time as "chronic stressors." He said an example of that would be, "taking care of a family member who is disabled..."[5]

Seeing it from that perspective, I realized I was not only being affected by the issues that arose day to day, but by the stress of the journey itself. Thankfully, it was becoming apparent that when I could use mindfulness to find ways to be with what was happening, seeing it as it was in the moment without reacting out of old patterns and beliefs, I was able to be with the situations more easily. I was also kinder when I interacted with Ron.

The future that we had imagined was clearly being detoured. No, diverted. We were never going to get back on the route that we planned. It was now a new journey of uncertainty, and I was discovering that there was no real map, only guideposts.

The journey unfolded as we traveled. I was learning that only by paying attention to what was happening along the route, did I know which way to go at the next turn. And there wasn't even a clearly defined destination, other than the fact that Ron would eventually die, but so would I. In the meantime, I would do my best to care for him.

As I look back on that period, I see how Ron must have been feeling stressed too. Just as the familiarity with my life was being disrupted due to trying to navigate our new life, so too, the ways of being that he had relied upon for his identity and comfort were no longer available to him.

It's hard enough for those of us whose minds are still functional not to be emotionally reactive when we feel threatened on some level. But what about Ron and others who are the ones wrestling with the disease?

The day he went to work at the garden shop when it was his day off and the day he walked to the School for the Blind when he was not scheduled to work, he was just doing what was familiar to him. I was learning that striving for familiarity was common among those with Alzheimer's and that made sense. I could see it in myself, as well.

At one of the meetings of our support group, a woman whose husband had been a professor at the local college told us how he would routinely walk to the campus and go to the area where his office had been to see if he had any mail. The staff didn't know how to manage him and as time went on, his safety was at risk since he had to cross a busy street to get to the campus.

She tried limiting his ability to leave the house but that only heightened his agitation. She tried going with him, but he didn't like that. After all, she hadn't gone with him when he was teaching. Eventually she decided to place him in a facility so she could be comfortable knowing that he was safe, thereby reducing her stress, as well.

At another meeting, Jerry shared about a situation with his wife who was trying to do what she had always done. He explained that before he went to take a nap one day, he put some chicken that he was going to cook for dinner on the kitchen counter to finish thawing. In the meantime, his wife got up from her nap and when she saw the chicken, decided that she was going to make dinner which was a familiar routine. After all, she was the wife and that was her role.

When Jerry got up, he found that every surface in the kitchen was covered with things she had gotten out of the cupboards and refrigerator, evidently trying to find something that would make sense to her. The biggest surprise was that she also went to the garage, where she found a bag of poop they had collected when they took their dog for a walk. She had been cutting pieces of the poop on the cutting board along with the chicken. So much for that meal—not to mention the project he then had in putting everything away and cleaning up. And, of course, he had to throw out the knife and cutting board.

I can't imagine what the bitch might have said had Ron done something similar. Thankfully, in beginning to see his behavior from a whole new perspective, I could see that he couldn't help it and didn't even understand what he was doing. That was clearly the case with my friends' spouses. They were just trying to be comfortable and do what they had routinely done, prior to their brains being affected by Alzheimer's. It was becoming clear that my involvement with the Alzheimer's Association was helping me gain a much better understanding of Ron's behavior.

In addition to deepening my understanding of the disease, mindfulness was helping as well. When I was able to pay more attention to the times when I got stressed, I became more comfortable "being with" it instead of scrambling to get a plan or finding a way to fix it and get it right. Those ways of seeing things may have helped me earlier in my life, but the limitations were becoming clear, especially in this situation.

A fundamental aspect of the teachings of Jon Kabat-Zinn, was using mindfulness to see things newly and interact with them differently. By being present, we can let go of our habitual ways of seeing things and doing things. When we are aware of our experience, he described how we can *respond* to what is occurring instead of *react* out of old habits. That was exactly what I was learning to do.

As I continued to incorporate mindfulness into my life, it was becoming clear that, on this journey into unknown territory with Ron, when the bitch showed up, I was reacting due to my own fear and discomfort. However, in understanding more about the disease, when I could be present with whatever was occurring as opposed to seeing situations as I might have previously seen them, it was easier to respond.

In *Full Catastrophe Living*, Kabat-Zinn says, "The very first and most important step in breaking free from... stress reactivity is to be mindful of what is happening, while it is happening."[6] He explained that when we become aware of ourselves getting hooked into the emotions which often accompany stressful events, it's helpful not to try and change it or pretend it's not happening, but to take a breath and become aware of the physical sensations and emotions that we are experiencing. Doing that, helps us relax and choose a different response.

Kabat-Zinn referred to the work of Dr. Martin Seligman, that indicated, "it is not the potential stressor itself but how you perceive it and then how you handle it that will determine whether or not it will lead to stress."[7]

Though I didn't have time to start meditating again, I tried to incorporate mindfulness into the experiences I was having by becoming aware of them while they were occurring. It was not easy, but I could clearly see that behaving as the bitch was a *reaction* to situations when I felt threatened or inconvenienced in some way. Perhaps the most important part of being the one who had to change, would involve developing the skills to see it differently and *respond*.

Even trips to the grocery store could be filled with opportunities to practice being present. In order to keep track of Ron more easily, I asked him to push the grocery cart and just follow me. One day when we were in the produce section and I was putting some mushrooms into the cart, Ron said, "It's about time we had something good to eat."

When he said that, I could feel the anger pulsing through my body. I always made good meals that he enjoyed. In fact, in the days before Alzheimer's, he routinely complimented me on my cooking. I could see myself wanting to ask him, "When was the last time you had a bad meal?" then say something about just ordering fast food from now on. The bitch would have made an appearance and I would have reacted.

Thankfully, being in a public location helped mitigate what I might have said had we been at home, as I forgot about paying attention to my breath or being aware of the sensations and emotions I was experiencing. Though irritated, I was able to calmly tell Ron about what I was planning to make with the mushrooms and went on shopping.

That experience illustrated the point that it's the way we perceive the situation, versus our life actually being in danger, that is stressful. It was not what was happening, but the way I was seeing it.

Having grown up in the era where I was striving to be a housewife like June Cleaver, being a good cook was not only one of the ways I defined myself, but it was also an important way to look good and do it right in the process. And now my husband didn't think I was a good cook! Ron's statement clearly threatened the reality upon which I had based my identity. No wonder I was pissed.

I began to see that, in many of the other instances where the bitch showed up, the comfort I got by thinking I had things under control was being threatened. Yet, I could no longer maintain that way of going about life with Ron, as I had no clue what was going to happen next, and I was fooling myself by trying to keep it under control.

On another occasion, one Sunday evening when Ron was watching a football game, I told him I was going to bed since I had to get up early to go to work the next day. I went upstairs, got into bed and fell asleep. When I woke up at 2:00 a.m., Ron wasn't in bed. I panicked, wondering what I was going to find when I went down to the living room, or if he would even be there. But there he was, sitting on the couch half asleep with the TV screen in a holding pattern. Clearly, he didn't know what to do after the game was over, if he even knew it was over, so he just sat there. At least he hadn't left the house, hurt himself, or caused some sort of damage. Had I been more skilled in caring for him at that time, I would not have left him alone in the first place.

When I turned off the TV and invited him to come to bed, he continued to sit, looking totally confused and kind of miffed at me for bothering him. Again, my immediate reaction would have been for the bitch to say something to him. I was pissed. I didn't have time for this. Thankfully, I then remembered to take a breath and got myself calmed down enough so I could respond more skillfully.

Little by little I coaxed him to get up and come to bed so he would be warmer and more comfortable. I was beginning to see that as I practiced responding, I was learning to find a balance between overseeing things and being more directive, while at the same time being Ron's partner and not his boss.

Then there was the evening that summer, when I accidently left the car unlocked in the driveway. Ron thought we were at his parents' house in Nebraska and had gotten in, ready to drive us home. I couldn't get him to budge, even after offering to drive us myself. So much for thinking I had a plan and knew what to do next.

I could feel my impatience with both myself and Ron, and my mind was racing. I finally stopped trying to figure out what to do and just stood there, feeling my anxiety. I took a few breaths, then I remembered something from a class I attended that was offered by the Alzheimer's Association.

I learned that at times it was necessary to do what to me seemed manipulative. That involved totally changing the focus and sometimes telling little lies to get folks with Alzheimer's to cooperate.

So, I told Ron that I noticed a strange noise in the car when I took his mom to the store yesterday, and I thought we should have a mechanic look at it before we drove back to Colorado. That convinced him to get out of the car and he went in the house with me. He was clearly tired, so he was then cooperative in getting ready for bed when I redirected him.

The more I relied on what I was learning in the classes and practiced being mindful, the more my ability to be with Ron seemed to improve. I was seeing that when I let go of my negative assessments of a situation, and saw it differently, I responded in a different way.

When I came across the words of Tara Brach, a psychologist and meditation teacher, in an article in which she had been interviewed, I could relate. She said, "Our habit is usually to view challenging situations as if something is wrong; that we are a victim and we have a problem. What if instead of a problem, we perceive stress as a signal to call on our resourcefulness, intelligence, care and courage?"[8]

Wow, that made this change that I was engaged in sound like a very worthwhile endeavor. Those qualities certainly resonated with me as something that I'd like to develop. And it helped remind me that in being aware of what I was thinking, I could reframe the way I was perceiving it.

It was becoming very apparent that when I was reacting as the bitch, it eliminated any possibility of discovering that there may even be some good times on our journey. As time went on, I began to see that as a result of being with whatever was happening, I was also developing the ability to be more present when tender moments occurred.

On Saturday mornings, Ron always liked to listen to "All Things Considered" on NPR. One weekend they were interviewing Barry Petersen, a CBS journalist who had written a book, *Jan's Story*, about his journey with his wife who had younger onset dementia. I was cleaning up the kitchen and when I heard what they were discussing, I joined Ron in the living room.

At the end of the interview, Barry talked about the time he went to visit his wife when she was in a facility, and she asked him to marry her. That brought tears to Ron's eyes. I told him that story was about a couple like us who were dealing with Alzheimer's, and then he really started to cry. For a short while he seemed to be aware of his predicament and when I took his hand and said, "I'm sorry," he said, "That's life and we will be okay." A few minutes later, in referring to our cat Eliot who was lying on the sofa, Ron said, "I wonder if he knows I'm a goofball?"

By that time, I was crying too. Though it wasn't the way it had been prior to Alzheimer's, I was thankful that I was able to feel emotionally connected with him in that conversation.

Chapter 6

I COULD SEE THAT I was going to have many opportunities to practice reframing the situations in which I found myself so as not to see them as a problem. As I got better at becoming aware of my habitual and unhelpful thoughts when they arose, I continued to see the value of mindfulness in helping me reduce the stress I was experiencing.

I remember Jon Kabat-Zinn saying, "You can't stop the waves, but you can learn to surf,"[1] in reference to using mindfulness to avoid being swept under by stressful events.

If I could see the events with Ron in the context of learning to surf, maybe I could eventually learn to ride the waves of this Alzheimer's journey. That would also include remembering to take a breath if I felt like I was going to be swept under.

I then came across something else Tara Brach said, that described what I seemed to be experiencing. She said, "Resilience grows when we become intentional about bringing our best to difficult life seasons."[2]

I later saw an article defining resilience as, "the ability to get back up after adversity." It described resilient people having the ability "to greet change and difficulty as an opportunity for self-reflection, learning, and growing." It also cited a study where it was found that people who are mindful are better at coping in difficult situations "... without becoming overwhelmed or shutting down (emotionally)."[3]

Evidently as I got better at surfing, I would become more resilient too. The surfing analogy was a good reminder because learning to surf takes a lot of practice, as did caring for Ron.

I was discovering that surfing involved quickly evaluating the elements of each situation. I couldn't stop the waves and each one was different. I often had to adjust my expectations and approaches on the spot so as not to "wipeout."

By the time Ron had Alzheimer's for several years, I seemed to be catching on to the fact that anything could happen and most of it was beyond my control. Though there were times when I seemed able to pause and observe my thoughts and feelings, there were still occasions when, instead, I was challenged by his behaviors, felt like I didn't have a clue what to do, or wished that it would all just go away and get back to "normal."

As his disease progressed, the challenges escalated, giving me and the family no end of opportunities to practice surfing.

One Sunday morning, about a year after we all had been trying to come to terms with Ron having Alzheimer's, Tom was in town. He was going to take his dad out to breakfast then spend the morning with him. That meant I could have some time to myself when I didn't have to keep an eye on Ron. I was looking forward to that. I had been wanting to clean out some things that were accumulating in the basement.

They had only been gone a little over an hour when Tom called. He said they were already on their way home, as, after breakfast when they were walking around the park, his dad pooped in his pants. That was a first. So much for my plan. The rare gift of time for myself was being cut short and I was feeling both puzzled and perturbed when they arrived.

Ron sat in the passenger seat which Tom had covered with a plastic bag in order to get home, though of course sitting only made matters worse. As we helped him into the bathroom and began cleaning him up,

I suddenly realized I hadn't done that since Aleah was a toddler. Clearly, this was different. I felt squeamish and wondered if I was up for the task. Tom was next to me, also taken by surprise about what had happened. I was glad I wasn't alone. We improvised as we began the project.

First, I took off Ron's shoes and handed them to Tom and then his slacks. Thankfully, having learned something like this could happen in the classes I was taking, I had gotten a box of medical gloves. They came in handy that day. Tom later said he was relieved when he saw I had those. We eventually finished the clean-up by helping Ron with a shower.

When we had him dressed in clean clothes again, I noticed that he didn't seem particularly concerned. Maybe that was because he didn't understand or even remember what happened. I thought he would have at least been embarrassed, but that was the Ron I used to know.

While we were cleaning him up, Tom told me that at the restaurant when they finished eating, his dad said he had to go to the bathroom. After helping him find the restroom, which was a one-seater, Tom stayed there, averting his eyes as Ron sat on the toilet. When it became clear that might be hindering the process, Tom said he stepped into the hallway hoping that would speed things up, while guarding the unlocked door.

A line was forming, and he explained to those waiting that his dad had Alzheimer's. Yet, the possibility of his dad being constipated, and the lengthening line of men, spurred him on. Tom said he eventually felt he had to help Ron get up and let others use the bathroom. He then paid the bill, and they left the restaurant to take a walk.

He went on to tell me, after they had walked about a block, Ron told him he was going to poop. Tom said he tried to get him to hurry back to the restaurant hoping they could request an urgent need for the bathroom, but his dad was shuffling, trying not to have an accident.

Tom said, "At one point I thought it would be good to change the subject, so since we were walking on the sunny side of the street, I suggested that we sing that song together. A couple minutes later, in a combination of relief and disappointment, Dad announced that he lost the battle."

Tom told me Ron didn't seem too concerned, in fact he was perhaps relieved, as he added some new lyrics, singing, "crap running down my leg on the sunny side of the street." In spite of what happened, he said, "Dad was so funny and sweet."

I was stumped. I had learned that incontinence of urine and stool could be part of the Alzheimer's journey, yet I did not see indications of it with Ron until that morning. In fact, the literature indicated that incontinence of stool often didn't show up until the middle and especially, the late stage. He wasn't that far along in the disease, yet.

Then several months later, I went upstairs to check on Ron one Sunday morning while he was showering in the old claw foot tub. I discovered that he'd had another "accident," this time in the bathtub.

Again, I felt overwhelmed and almost gagged. The drain had gotten plugged, and the water was rising. No one else was there, so it was entirely up to me. The first step was clear. I needed to turn off the water, so the tub wouldn't overflow.

Having done that, I seemed able to let go of feeling quite so overwhelmed. I paused and took a breath to assess the situation. I helped Ron get out of the tub onto a towel, then had him sit on the toilet and gave him a magazine. After getting him situated, I improvised, proceeding step by step until I had the bathtub cleaned up and filled with water to which I had added some disinfectant so it could soak for a while. When I finished with the tub, I got him clean and dry, helped him get dressed, and took his hand so we could go downstairs to eat breakfast and move on with our day.

As a result of those experiences, when describing some of my challenges in navigating my new journey as Ron's care partner to my friends, I adjusted my comments. In addition to speaking about not knowing what was going to happen next or how long it would last, and not being able to fix it, I added, "and shit happens."

I was beginning to see that when faced with the events associated with Alzheimer's, I was transitioning to a whole new way of dealing with life. Besides being unfamiliar with what was happening and not knowing what to do, I was afraid. Just like surfing, I had to evaluate each wave instead of continuing to compartmentalize things into familiar categories so I could be comfortable, as I had done in the past.

In *Full Catastrophe Living*, Kabat-Zinn explained, "The alarm reaction enables us to call upon the full power of all our internal resources in life-threatening situations."[4] When shit happened, the stress hormones that would have enabled me to fight, flee or freeze to ensure my safety were activated. Neither Ron nor I were in real danger, but the situation certainly required that I take immediate action.

It would not have served any purpose to fight him, even with verbal remarks, and I wasn't going to flee and leave him there by himself. Certainly, in that situation, freezing and not taking any action was not an option, so there I was. It turned out that was a big wave I could surf to practice being present and resolving the issue on the spot. I guess that's how resilience works.

As I reflect on our Alzheimer's journey, I can see how, just when I thought I had gotten used to dealing with one of Ron's new behaviors, it would change. I remembered hearing that change is the only constant in life, but guess I never really put it to the test. I now see how that applies to life all the time, but we're so good at normalizing it from day to day, we often don't notice the changes.

At times I still saw myself trying to find a new normal, but Ron's behaviors were generally short-lived, and before I knew it, he would do something entirely different. Clearly, I was being given many opportunities to practice letting go of the way I thought things should be and be with what was actually occurring. Not only was the bitch fading into the background, but I was exploring new territory and discovering a fortitude in myself, of which I had not previously been aware. Guess I was becoming resilient.

Following the incident that Sunday morning, I was able to step back and see more clearly how Ron's incontinence was related to Alzheimer's. I was beginning to understand that evidently he could either no longer recognize the urge to have a bowel movement, or he was not able to determine what actions to take when he had that sensation. Clearly, he couldn't help it.

I saw the value of what I had been doing to familiarize myself with the disease and the resources, organizations, and people I could call upon for support. That helped me understand what was happening and do my best. When "shit happened," thankfully, I was at least aware that could occur.

When we were a little further along in the journey, I attended a workshop sponsored by the Alzheimer's Association in which Sara Qualls, Ph.D., who was associated with the Aging Center at the University of Colorado in Colorado Springs, offered a detailed account of the disease and how those caring for a loved one can best manage.[5]

The part of her presentation that I found most interesting was the chart she showed indicating how the stages of decline for a person with Alzheimer's are opposite the developmental stages for infants and toddlers (Appendix 1). Infants start out wearing diapers while adults with Alzheimer's usually end up wearing diapers due to incontinence. The first food that infants take in is sucked through a nipple then they graduate to soft baby food. On the other hand, adults with Alzheimer's often end up eating food that has been pureed and sucking liquids which have been thickened, through a straw. Likewise, as infants develop, they eventually learn to walk. Until then, they are either carried or pushed in a stroller. Adults with Alzheimer's often are unable to walk in the later stages and end up either in bed or being pushed in a wheelchair.

Overall, the chart showed how an "impaired elder" begins their journey with full autonomy and ends with a guardian who has primary responsibility for them. Clearly, it is just the opposite when an infant matures into childhood and beyond, as they become more autonomous.

Even though Ron was requiring more and more care that resembled the care needs of an infant, he was an adult. He was my husband. My intention was to treat him with the dignity he deserved, no matter what happened. It would have been easy to use baby talk or scold him, but I was careful not to do that. I tried my best to speak directly when caring for him, making eye contact and letting him know what I was doing.

When I was able to see Ron's behavior from a larger perspective, it was easier not to take things personally and to observe what was occurring with curiosity. Then I was able to take what seemed like the best action at the time with the knowledge I had. Again, like the surfer analogy, with Alzheimer's each event had its own unique qualities that needed to be taken into consideration on the spot.

Though incontinence of stool can certainly be a part of the journey, in Ron's case, those incidents seemed premature. I wondered if he needed to begin using Depends when he was still going to the bathroom on his own most of the time. I had also learned about the importance of helping the person with Alzheimer's maintain their independence and dignity as long as possible.

As a result, I chose not to have Ron wear Depends regularly, since those two incidents when he was incontinent of stool, were isolated. In making that choice, it seemed like it was treating him with dignity.

I realized that in deciding not to have Ron wear Depends, it would be good if I were to keep an eye out for cues so I could help him become aware of his need to go to the bathroom. It seemed like he may have been losing the ability to do that for himself.

I recall one evening when we were having dinner, he suddenly stood up and became restless for no apparent reason. I had a hunch and when I asked him if he needed to use the bathroom, he said "yes," so I helped him with that. Thankfully, I was getting better at being with things as they were occurring, instead of stuck in the way I thought it was supposed to be. Otherwise, I may have been focused on getting him to sit down so he could finish eating, which would have resulted in a mess to clean up.

In talking to my friend Wayne, whose wife also had Alzheimer's, he mentioned having to be sensitive to what our spouses were going through and then adapt. That was a good way of explaining what I became aware of when I saw that I was the one who had to change. Learning to adapt... over and over again.

Thus, as I let go of the previous rules by which I had lived and learned to be with the uncertainty of the situations that were occurring, I was adapting. As a result, I was experiencing more energy, as well as developing more resilience to deal with the situations that arose.

Thankfully, not every day brought a particularly unsettling issue to deal with. But every day there was something with which I could practice getting out of my habitual ways of seeing the issues as a problem.

One of the frequent events occurred every time we left the house to drive somewhere. After we went about a block Ron would ask, "Where are we going?" even though I had already told him while we were getting ready to leave. When I could pause and step back from the bitch saying something like, "How many times do I have to tell you?" or being sarcastic in some way, and just answer the question, there was a lot less drama for both of us.

As we drove on, he usually continued to ask the same question over and over. It worked best when I could just answer the question over and over and tell him where we were going, as if I was telling him for the first time. Sometimes it almost seemed like a game.

The value of what I was learning and the effort I was putting forth was confirmed during one of the times when Ron was lucid. As he was getting into bed one night, he made a comment about his kids "having a dad who's so fucked up." He then apologized for being so much trouble, both for me and for those who came to help care for him. I told him we were all doing our best to help him enjoy his life and said that I was learning a lot in the process. He replied, saying he appreciated all I was doing.

Since it was one of the few times that felt like we were having a normal conversation, I asked if there was anything else I could do that would make it easier for him.

He said, "Just keep loving me—it means a lot." He went on to say, "I didn't want it to turn out this way but, it is what it is." Then he told me, "You need to take care of yourself first, then take care of me." It sounded like he had been in the classes I was attending, where we were continually reminded to take care of ourselves.

I was moved to tears when we shared such tender moments as that conversation, and though infrequent, they helped me appreciate my choice to stay with Ron and be his care partner. His sweet words that night deepened my commitment to the journey we were on, and as we continued, remembering them helped me when the rough times occurred.

Chapter 7

As I KEPT ADAPTING TO the process of his decline, the changes in Ron's behavior and needs often resulted in more for me to do and additional expenses. Those changes also required further acknowledgement that the Ron I knew was slipping away. It was becoming easier for me to understand, interact, and be flexible in response to his decline most of the time, but occasionally, I still saw myself wanting to hold onto the way things had been. I was surprised at the strength of that pattern.

In the past, I often felt like it reflected poorly on me if I was not able to step up to the plate and handle something on my own without asking for help. But in the classes I had been taking through the Alzheimer's Association, I was hearing over and over about the importance of us care partners looking after ourselves. They always used the analogy about flying, when parents are reminded to put their oxygen mask on first before helping a child who might be traveling with them.

In other words, if I was too tired and burned out, how could I be there for Ron? I needed to take care of myself, as he reminded me when he was getting into bed that night. The idea of putting myself first felt new to me, though.

Along those lines, one of the things I also learned about was to periodically take our loved one to a facility for a week or two. That was referred to as "respite care." When I heard a woman in my support group describe how helpful it was to have time alone when her husband was being cared for in a facility, I decided to look into it. After all, I thought there may come a time when I would like to leave town for a retreat or need to focus my full attention on something without being distracted by looking after Ron.

I researched the facilities where respite care was available for individuals with memory impairment and eventually found one where it seemed like I would be comfortable leaving him, so I took time off work to check it out. I decided it would be best for our first experience to do it when I would be around most of the time so I could be available in case something happened.

On the day I had reserved for his stay to begin, I packed his bag with his clothes and toiletries. When we arrived at the facility, I helped Ron get settled in his room. Since it was the first time using respite care, I went to dinner with him to help ease the transition for both of us. After dinner, I went home with both a heaviness and a lightness in my heart. I was looking forward to being able to focus on my job, keep my own schedule, and get out of town to visit my friend, Karen, over the weekend. Yet, it would also be the first time since this journey began that I would be away from Ron for an extended period.

I was curious about having time to myself. Before his symptoms of Alzheimer's began, I had enjoyed a certain amount of independence in my life. Even though we were married and did many things together, we were each involved in our own separate activities. Now with him having Alzheimer's, I felt more alone since I could no longer have conversations with him or relate as we had done in the past. Yet, on the other hand, I felt more tied to him.

Not only was I losing Ron, but it also felt, in a way, like I was losing myself. So, time just for me was important, not only in getting a break from the responsibilities and having some down time. It was also important in connecting with myself and discovering the new strengths I was gaining in being Ron's care partner.

Though, I only went to see Karen for a couple of days and otherwise stayed home and went to work, I enjoyed having the time to focus on my own needs for a change. I could even take time to meditate.

During Ron's stay at the facility, I checked with them several times and was reassured that everything seemed to be going well. On the day I went to pick him up, I arrived early in the afternoon. He was standing at the front door with his bag packed and the slacks he was wearing were wet.

The staff said they told him I would be coming to get him that day, so he got up early. They said that even though they told him I wasn't coming until after lunch, he insisted on waiting at the door the whole time. They couldn't budge him. It was a tender moment when I arrived. Ron was clearly very glad to see me. Likewise, I was glad to see him and hugged him despite his wet pants. Luckily, I had a towel in the car, so I put it on the passenger seat before helping him get in.

When we got home, I helped him take a shower then put on some clean, dry clothes. As I unpacked his bag, I discovered that all his undershorts had been stuffed in the end pockets and they were wet with urine. I sighed in anticipation of another significant change in our lives. I kept an eye on Ron over the next few days, and it was apparent that, even though he was home again, he was incontinent of urine most of the time.

The Alzheimer's Association website indicates, "Incontinence can be caused by the inability to recognize the need to use the restroom, forgetting where the bathroom is, and side effects from medicine."[1] In Ron's case, it appeared to be the inability to recognize the urge to urinate.

He confirmed that one evening when I was helping him get ready for bed. I asked him if he had to pee, and he said, as he went to stand in front of the toilet, "I don't know. If I stand here and pee comes out, then I had to pee. If I stand here and nothing happens, then I didn't." The cleverness and wisdom in what he said made me giggle.

Though there had not been any additional incidents involving incontinence of stool, it was clear that the time had come for him to wear Depends regularly. There I was again, relying on what I had learned about Alzheimer's, recognizing that I was going to be even more involved in his care, and at the same time, experiencing another loss of the man I had known.

The losses, though varied, were becoming more frequent. Thankfully, with my mindfulness practice, I was learning to be more accepting of the feelings that were arising, many of which I had tried to avoid throughout my life. The day when he went wandering and was eventually found at the movie theater downtown, I experienced an intense six-hour session in hanging out with fear, anger, and sadness, as I had no idea how it was going to turn out.

After Ron's wandering event, especially since it became public knowledge, I could see the tendency to criticize myself. I wondered how I could have been so stupid and irresponsible as to let that happen. Thankfully, as I became aware of myself doing that, I was reminded of the teachings of Kristen Neff, whose work focused on self-compassion. She spoke of the value of mindfully observing our thoughts and feelings as they are.

She wrote, "Self-compassion entails being warm and understanding toward ourselves when we suffer, fail, or feel inadequate, rather than ignoring our pain or flagellating ourselves with self-criticism."[2]

She also noted the importance of understanding that "being imperfect, failing, and experiencing life difficulties is inevitable."[3] I was beginning to see that since the Alzheimer's journey was filled with unfamiliar experiences, maybe I could cut myself a little slack and let it be okay not to know what to do and to make mistakes.

On her website, Kristen Neff also explains that "having compassion for oneself is really no different than having compassion for others."[4] In seeing how hard it was to have compassion for myself, I wondered if I would be able to apply it to the situations with Ron amid these crazy experiences.

However, I noticed that as I learned more about the disease and practiced being compassionate with myself, I was able to offer more understanding and kindness to Ron. The bitch didn't need to judge him. I was also beginning to see that I was doing the best I could. In developing my ability to let go of expectations and be with the feelings that arose when I was uncertain or felt like things were out of control, I could be more loving and present with each of us.

Sally Armstrong confirmed that. She pointed out that if we can stay in our discomfort instead of pushing through or repressing what we're feeling, especially in tough situations, we can learn "to trust the capacity of our ability to be with something that's really difficult."[5] She further indicated that being open to our suffering "tenderizes our heart and the heart becomes more responsive."[6]

In fact, in an article written by Linda Graham, MFT, entitled, "Mindfulness, Self-Compassion and Resilience" she stated that, "More compassion leads to more resilience."[7] It all seemed to be coming together.

Evidently, the more I could be present to all the feelings I was having in caring for Ron, the stronger I would be, and my heart would become more tender at the same time. Seems like in the past, I would have seen having a tender heart and being strong as a dichotomy.

Apparently, in the process of using mindfulness to be present and open to whatever was occurring, not only was I was learning to respond instead of react and become more resilient, I was also learning to have compassion for both Ron and myself. It helped to understand that we were each doing our best.

Gradually, I was also seeing that when I could use whatever was happening as something from which I could learn, I had more energy. Trying to control, avoid, or get it right, drained my energy. When I accepted the challenge of being the one who had to change, I stepped into a very fertile training ground. In expanding my ability to be with whatever was occurring as best I could, I was learning to experience life more fully.

I was also discovering that when I could see things differently and be more open, I could take better care of Ron. Having learned about wandering from the classes I was taking, then having experienced it firsthand the day he went to the movies, I began to think more about what other precautions I could take.

In addition to adjusting the gates so they couldn't be opened when secured with a lock, I made sure the deadbolt locks that were on the front and back doors required a key on the inside as well as the outside, then I kept the key.

I remember when I shared about doing that at my support group, another woman said she couldn't do that as it would mean she was locking her husband up. I explained that the way I saw it, we were no longer playing by the same rules, and it was necessary to shift our perspectives. Things had changed and we needed to keep our husbands safe so they couldn't get out. It was far different from locking them up.

The importance of seeing things in a different context applied to many things on the Alzheimer's journey. Gradually, as I began to understand how Ron might be seeing things, I let go of trying to convince him otherwise. Therein was the opportunity for me to hang out in the unknown, explore another perspective, and respond compassionately. Thankfully, the bitch was slowing fading into the background.

As he continued to decline, I found myself needing to take more and more responsibility for Ron's life, doing what was necessary to ensure his safety and well-being. That fit perfectly with what Sara Qualls indicated in her diagram comparing the decline in Alzheimer's patients with the maturation of infants. Some of the choices were obvious, such as having him wear Depends and locking the gates and doors, while others were more complicated.

I was discovering that getting involved with his medical issues required making choices where I was taking even more responsibility for Ron's life.

He had been getting colonoscopies more frequently than every ten years due to having polyps. When I remembered that he was due for one about two years into our journey, I was tormented in considering the pros and cons of scheduling that. How could I get him to drink the required amount of laxative to thoroughly clean out his intestines for the procedure? Then if he drank it, I could imagine the mess due to him not being able to get to the toilet in time. I even talked to the gastroenterologist about admitting him to the hospital for that. I did my best to weigh all the options.

Finally, I decided that I was not going to have him get a colonoscopy. But what if that resulted in him getting colon cancer? It was hard enough to make such decisions regarding my own health, but now I was making them for Ron, and he could not even discuss the matter.

I talked to his kids, but I was the one who was going to be impacted. Eventually, I rationalized that, with Alzheimer's, he was probably going to die sooner than he would have otherwise, so why worry? That seemed like a reasonable perspective, though it felt harsh, and I still had doubts about my decision.

A similar issue arose related to Ron's sleep apnea. A year or two before he began to show symptoms of memory impairment, he started using a CPAP machine. Periodically, he would take it apart and clean it, but I noticed that as time went on, he was no longer doing that.

One Saturday, I forced myself to take time to read the instructions that were next to the machine. They described the bacteria and mold that can grow in it, especially if it is not disassembled and given a thorough cleaning at least once a week. So, I began the cleaning process that was described. I was startled by the buildup of sludge that I found. Now, I would have to schedule time for that chore on the weekends along with everything else that I was doing to maintain our household.

Then, during the next couple of months I was routinely being awakened in the middle of the night by the noise of the CPAP running. As long as Ron was wearing it, it didn't bother me, but when he got up to go to the bathroom, he would leave the headpiece laying on the bed unattached and would not turn off the machine. I was pissed. I had to get up to go to work the next day.

I asked him repeatedly to please turn it off as he had done in the past, but nothing changed. After being with the situation over the next few weeks and having my sleep regularly interrupted, it became clear that Ron's Alzheimer's was keeping him from remembering to turn off the CPAP machine. Between that and having to clean it, I decided this was a situation in which I needed to put on my own oxygen mask.

I surprised myself in that I didn't call Ron's doctor to consult with him. I just decided to get rid of the CPAP machine then and there. I cleaned it one last time and after learning the company that provided it would not be able to reuse it, I checked and found an organization in the community that provided used medical equipment to those with low income.

One day, I took time off work to deliver it, and that was that. My life was simplified, my sleep was no longer interrupted, I helped someone else, and Ron didn't know the difference.

Such action would have felt irresponsible to me in the past, but this was another lesson in learning to see things differently. Previously, taking a stand for my own health and well-being in such a situation would have seemed selfish, but I was seeing the importance of doing that in caring for Ron.

Chapter 8

IN ADDITION TO NEEDING TO take more responsibility for Ron's medical care and my own well-being, the classes I was taking highlighted the value of making sure that our legal and financial papers were in order. Though we had gotten our wills and powers of attorney done years ago prior to me having brain surgery, we hadn't kept them updated.

The "business" side of life was never of much interest to me. However, in working at the hospital, I was aware of the complications and stress that arose for families when people were admitted in an emergency and didn't have current legal documents in place, especially a medical power of attorney. I didn't want that to happen to us.

It was clear that I needed to make Aleah my power of attorney since Ron could no longer perform such a task, though I would continue as his power of attorney. That was easy enough. But the will itself felt more complicated, especially since Ron and I married mid-life with children from previous marriages.

I checked out the local attorneys, some of whom I had seen at events sponsored by the Alzheimer's Association or other senior programs in the community. Knowing that there was a limited period in which Ron would be able to sign his name, I began to feel a sense of urgency. On top of that, my lack of experience and confidence in doing such things resulted in that being one of the more challenging aspects of my new role.

As I ventured into unfamiliar territory, I was reminded over and over of the importance of looking out for myself, this time financially, since I was probably going to be the one who survived. I was beginning to see the value of what I was contributing to Ron and his family by caring for him. Thus, I tried to make decisions that were in my own best interest while ensuring that Ron would receive the care he needed and, at the same time, not be selfish with his assets.

I was also seeing that there were many approaches to the preparation of legal documents. Some attorneys offered "bells and whistles," such as albums and other ways of memorializing the individual, while others were pretty cut and dried.

Eventually, I learned that it was advisable to set up a will with a "marital trust" to provide care for Ron should I die before he did. That made sense. He would need someone to oversee his care as I had been doing.

I was relieved when I finally completed the legal paperwork, though I was not fond of going through the process and it was time consuming, not to mention costly. But I learned a lot.

Aside from becoming more knowledgeable about the legal issues and numerous ways of addressing them, I saw how much easier it would have been had Ron and I routinely reviewed the documents and kept them up to date. But it was also easy to ignore and even deny the importance of such matters—especially when they involved facing the fact that we were eventually going to die or that one of us may end up with a condition for which we needed to receive care, as was occurring with Ron.

Then there were our finances. We were aware of each other's financial situation, but after we married, we kept our money, and our investments, separate. We primarily just shared our routine living expenses and purchased our house together.

Over the years, Ron had done a better job of accumulating his resources and investing them than I had. I was glad for that as I was beginning to see that his care could be costly. There were many things to consider that I needed to learn about and incorporate into our lives, though there were few absolutes.

In addition to the legal and financial aspects, I was becoming aware that every situation in life seemed complicated by Ron having Alzheimer's, and I didn't always use my best judgement. Sometimes I was tired, sometimes I was busy, sometimes I just didn't want to be bothered, sometimes I still wanted to pretend it wasn't happening, and sometimes I didn't know any better.

One Sunday, about a year and a half into our journey, all those factors seemed to come into play.

Ron's brother Max, his wife, and their friends were going to stop by our house for brunch on their way to New Mexico. They lived in California, and I was looking forward to it being a special occasion.

Prior to their arrival, I was busy making the meal and preparing the table. I asked Ron to bring some extra chairs up from the basement as he always had done when we had guests. But when time passed and I looked down the stairs, I saw him just standing there staring, not bringing the chairs up. I thought he was just confused so I went down and carried them up myself. When he came up, I could tell there was something else going on.

He said he was tired, so he went upstairs to take a nap until they arrived, and I continued with the meal preparation.

Not long after Ron laid down our guests arrived, so I went up and got him. He seemed glad to see them and acted hospitable, but still, something seemed a bit off—even different from his typical Alzheimer's days.

We all sat down in the dining room and enjoyed quiche, muffins, fruit, and coffee, while Max updated us on his life. Then Ron suddenly got up and went into the bathroom. I followed him due to his seeming urgency. He made it to the toilet just in time to throw up. That was unusual. I then suggested that he go lie down again, and I went back into the dining room and excused him. We talked a little longer, then everyone left.

I cleaned up the kitchen and checked on Ron. He was sleeping soundly, and I needed to get something at the grocery store, so I left him alone. I made sure the doors were locked and since I had gotten them keyed on the inside, I was sure to take the keys. When I got home, he was still sleeping, and I went ahead and made dinner. When Ron woke up, he seemed pretty normal, so we ate dinner and watched *60 Minutes* together. It was just like a regular Sunday evening.

The next day as I got ready for work, I was aware of some additional sluggishness and confusion with Ron. But it was Monday morning and I needed to keep moving. When Steve came to watch Ron, I suggested that he keep an eye on him and told him what happened the day before.

After I got to my office, which was in the hospital, I was telling my colleague, Jan, about the weekend. Her training was a bit more medically oriented than mine.

When she heard my description of Ron's behavior, she told me she thought I should go get him and bring him to the ER. Based on what she was saying, not only did his age put him at risk for numerous medical issues, but he was also no longer as active as he had once been, and he couldn't tell me about what he was experiencing. She said the vomiting incident could have been a side effect of any number of things. I was glad to have someone with whom I could consult. What she was saying made sense. I called Steve and told him that I was coming to get Ron immediately and asked him to have him ready when I got home.

It was a cool April morning and Ron was in the yard with Steve when I arrived. He had his jacket on and was ready to go. I realized that I needed to go in to get his medical card and ID information. When I came back out, he willingly got in the car and didn't seem like anything was bothering him while I drove back to the hospital.

I pulled up at the ER entrance so the valet could park the car. Ron and I got out and started walking toward the doors. He said he was cold, and I went a few steps ahead so that the automatic doors would open before he got there. As I passed through the entrance and approached the second doorway, I suddenly heard a muffled sound and a gasp from others in the area.

When I turned around, I saw Ron flat on the floor, face down—his glasses several feet away from his face. I picked up his glasses as I bent down to talk to him, but he didn't respond. I panicked! When I looked up, I saw a medical team with a gurney running toward us. I was thankful for that. Someone had already reported what happened.

Ron was unconscious as they loaded him on to the gurney. I was afraid, though also impressed with the medical expertise and speed with which they intervened. I stopped at the desk to register him, then a nurse took me to the room in the trauma unit where they were caring for him. By the time I got there, they had already ripped off his shirt and had him hooked up to monitors.

The doctor gave me a preliminary report of their findings, but they were still awaiting the lab results. He said it appeared that Ron had a DVT (deep venous thrombosis), probably located in his thigh, and a blood clot had separated and gotten into his bloodstream causing a pulmonary embolism, which can be fatal.

For a moment I was clear that had Jan not suggested I go home and get Ron, he probably would have died before the day was over. At the same time, deep inside my psyche, there was a conversation saying, "He's going to die anyway. We can't fix Alzheimer's." But that would have been too soon to lose Ron, and I would not have been able to forgive myself.

At times, due to what seemed like my hesitation in doing the right thing both the previous day and on that Monday morning, I struggled. What was I thinking? When I saw how tired and lethargic he was even before the guests arrived for brunch, I could have cancelled the whole thing and taken him to the ER then and there.

It seemed like it should have been clear, but it was complicated. Clearly, I was trying to hold onto "normal" and was in denial. Had something been bothering Ron, he would have mentioned it. That's the way it had always been.

Though his condition stabilized to some degree while he was in the ER, he still needed a significant amount of care, so he was admitted to ICU. When they got him settled there, I could see that he was beginning to get a very black eye as a result of the fall.

The nurses gave me cold compresses to hold on his eye to reduce the swelling and discoloration, which I did for much of the afternoon. Ron didn't understand what was happening, but luckily, he was somewhat sedated so he didn't try to push me away. Finally, I went home, exhausted, but knowing he was receiving good care.

After several days in the ICU, he improved enough to be transferred to a medical floor. Due to him being a potential wanderer, the hospital provided a sitter to be in his room. Luckily, I could go back to work, though I stopped by his room frequently, as well as before and after work.

During the time he was hospitalized the doctors were working to minimize the risk of further blood clots, then, after a total of ten days, he was discharged home with a list of all the things I had to manage.

Having been on his own to order the food for his meals during his hospitalization, Ron evidently ordered a lot of hamburgers and pie. He had gained about ten pounds. It didn't occur to me that I needed to get involved in helping with his food choices too. So being a shopper of secondhand items, I made a quick trip to the used clothing store.

There, I bought several pairs of the khaki slacks that he liked to wear, as well as another pair of jeans, all with a waist size a couple of inches larger than the ones he had been wearing.

Of primary importance at the time of his discharge was getting him on Coumadin to keep his blood thin enough so that clots didn't form, yet not put him at risk for serious bleeding. In order to ensure that he was receiving a safe and effective dose, a sample of his blood was checked in the lab using an INR (International Normalized Ratio) test to see if it was clotting adequately.

Immediately after going home, he began receiving care from visiting nurses who checked that and continued to make dosing adjustments so that he would get the correct amount. I was given a list of the foods that can increase the risk of bleeding as well as those that can inhibit the effectiveness of the Coumadin.

Several weeks later, we were on our own to get his INR checked at the outpatient clinic at the hospital. Then eventually, Ron's care and monitoring of the Coumadin were transferred to our primary care doctor where I took him once or twice a month to have it checked.

So much for the ways I had tried to minimize my responsibility and time in managing some of the medical issues involved in caring for Ron. I thought I had taken measures to simplify those by not having him get a colonoscopy and discontinuing his CPAP machine. But suddenly I had to take on more in managing his INR testing and providing a special diet.

How long would I be able to do this? Though I tried to step up to the challenges as best I could, they seemed to keep getting bigger. I wondered what would be next.

After Ron's hospitalization, I had some serious discussions with his kids about how to best go forward. We all clearly wanted him to be able to stay at home versus moving to a facility, but we now were looking more closely at his safety in our home environment.

What if, due to the instability he was experiencing as a result of the Alzheimer's, he was to fall down the stairs? And if he did fall, now that he was on Coumadin he would bleed more easily. Then there was the running up and down the stairs that I was doing to keep an eye on him.

After several more months of living with the questions that were arising and considering such things as moving our bedroom downstairs and living primarily on the main level of the house, it became clear.

One morning, as I was getting ready for work, I had a strong feeling that we needed to move to another house. If I was going to do that, I would no doubt qualify for a loan more easily while I was still working, as it was only a year until I would be sixty-five and could retire. It also seemed like, due to our situation, I would need to wait to put our current house on the market until after we moved as it would be difficult to show it to prospective buyers while we were still living there and caring for Ron. It was a big decision.

I talked to Curt. It was yet another thing to add to my plate with everything else I was trying to manage. But it became more and more clear that it was the right thing to do.

Within a couple of weeks, I found a realtor who was a friend of Kathryn's, and we defined the area of town in which I would consider living. She began showing me properties that were on the market. It was kind of exciting. I always loved looking at houses and imagining what it would be like to live in them.

Then, one day as I was driving home from work, I stumbled upon a house that had just been listed. I arranged for a showing, and it appeared to meet all my criteria. It was a '60s ranch-style and though it had a basement, it seemed like it would be easy enough to live primarily on the main floor and prevent Ron from going downstairs.

I had a few family members look at it with me and they agreed that it would work for us. No one else had made an offer yet, so I submitted my offer. After working with the realtor to negotiate a final price and get an inspection, we had a deal.

Thankfully, due to Ron's military service, he qualified for a VA loan which I took out in both of our names, then set a closing date. It all happened so fast and went so smoothly, I didn't worry about how I was going to manage the move and do everything that was needed. But at such times, it seemed that my mindfulness practice helped me stay present and not get ahead of myself.

I was able to sign all the papers electronically at work, just taking time off for the closing itself. I made sure I could represent both of us, as there was no way Ron could sit through that and I was not willing to manage him at such an event. I needed to put all my attention on what I was doing.

As a result, the closing took even longer than usual since, in addition to my own signature, I was signing on Ron's behalf as his power of attorney.

When I got home, a feeling of apprehension began to set in. I now owned two houses. I had a loan on one and the other was paid off. But would I be able to sell the old one? It wasn't a great housing market. The economy was in a slump. Yet, I had done what I knew I needed to do. I had to keep moving forward. Somehow this was going to work, even if I couldn't sell the old house and had to rent it after we moved.

Chapter 9

THE DAY AFTER THE CLOSING, I took Ron to the new house. I introduced us to the next-door neighbors then gave them my phone number.
The house was going to need a little work, primarily painting, before we
moved in. I figured I could do more updating after I retired.

I contacted Chris, a neighbor who was a contractor. He said that
he could oversee the work on the house before we moved in, then do
some updating on the old house before I put it on the market. He said
it would take about a month to get the painting done, after working it
into his schedule.

Of course, it would take me at least that long to get everything
packed up. I found a moving company and scheduled the date for the
move on January 2nd.

In the meantime, many friends and relatives asked me to let them
know if they could help. I remembered those who offered. I needed all
the help I could get. There was a special day coming up, Boxing Day
on December 26th, and I was excited to have a perfect way to celebrate

it. I was going to have everybody who offered their help come over to help with packing. When the day came, they brought their leftover Christmas food for snacks, as well as their extra boxes. We worked hard. Curt took Ron out so I didn't have to look after him at the same time.

I also contacted my cousin Jeff, who lived on a ranch not far from town. He told me to let him know if I needed anything. I could see that his horse trailer would be perfect for hauling the stuff from the basement and garage to the new house. He agreed and came to help the weekend before the move was scheduled. I was grateful that I was learning to ask for help and that I had many in my life who were kind enough to offer.

I made arrangements to take the first two weeks of January off work and to have Ron go to a local facility for respite care during part of that time. There was no way that I was going to keep track of him and oversee the move at the same time.

It was all coming together.

I spent the last night in our old house by myself. I felt sad and lonely without Ron, after purchasing that house together and sharing so many memories there. I was awakened shortly after midnight when the phone line was shut down, which set off the security alarm. I never went back to sleep.

When morning came, I got up and took the sheets off the bed then packed them before the movers arrived. Kathryn brought me a thermos of coffee. It was a brisk two degrees outside and had snowed less than an inch overnight. It was sunny and the snow on the ground was sparkling. I was struck by the beauty of the day and felt like it was a validation that I could do this too.

I had things pretty well marked so I could direct the moving crew where to put them in the new house, though several items still ended up in a random pile in the garage.

That evening I took the thermos back to Kathryn who invited me to stay for a bowl of soup, for which I was grateful after such a long day.

Following that, I went over to the old house to pick up Eliot, who had been confined to the bathroom all day with his litter box. After making sure the lights were off and it was all locked up, we had a procession to the new house with Kathryn's husband, Dave, driving my other car, Kathryn driving their car, and Eliot in the car with me.

Thankfully, they stayed to help me put my bed together. I could see I was going to miss having them in the neighborhood.

I was exhausted and slept well that night. When I looked out the window the next morning, I saw the beginning of a sunrise in the winter sky. It was a new and welcome experience to have the bedroom window facing east, as it had faced west in the old house. That was a good reminder that this journey with Ron was calling on me to discover a new way of seeing things. Everything seemed to be falling into place, yet at the same time, it felt like my life was falling apart. Big changes were underway.

I waited a few more days so I could get things organized a bit before I brought Ron home. I wanted to minimize as much of the chaos as possible so as not to have that add to whatever he was going to feel when suddenly he was thrust into a new environment. Thankfully, I had the locks changed right after I bought the house, and again had the dead bolt on the front door keyed on the inside. The back was a little more difficult to manage since it was a sliding glass door, but I put locks on the gates and had the security system installed.

The day I brought Ron home, he seemed at ease. He started to make comments about visiting Doug. Evidently our new house resembled the house where his friend from dental school had lived. Ron used to tell me that after his divorce, he would go visit Doug in Denver. Often, when I made dinner during the first week or two after bringing him home, he made a comment about what a good job I did finding things to cook in Doug's kitchen. I was glad he found a way to relate so he could be at ease with the experience. He, apparently, thought we were housesitting for Doug or something, and I supported that with my comments. He didn't seem to notice that eventually Doug never came home.

I found ways to let Ron help me unpack and set up places where he would be comfortable to sit and read or draw while I continued to get us settled before I had to go back to work. It was not long before he demonstrated a benefit I had not even noticed about the house.

The kitchen could be accessed by doorways on either side, and they were connected by a central hallway that went from the living room to the bedrooms. That meant there was a circle inside the house that involved going through the kitchen, and Ron was quick to find it. Just as he had walked around the other house outside in the yard, he could now walk circles inside our new home.

I assumed he liked that for the same reasons in that nothing changed from time to time, which seemed to help him feel more secure. I was grateful the house had that feature and he discovered it as a way to comfort himself. I understood. I could see how we all would like to have a life where things didn't change. But as I continued to replace my old routines with the new circumstances and challenges I was facing, I saw the benefits that the changes due to Ron's disease were offering in my own learning and growth.

The day came when I had to go back to work. After orienting Steve to the layout of the new house and location of the supplies, I left. The location was not quite as close to the hospital, so I factored in a little more time to get there.

In the coming weeks, with the help of my realtor, I focused on having a few improvements made to our old house so I could put it on the market. After listing it, I prepared myself to wait but was surprised when after only two weeks we had an offer which was acceptable. I was grateful and a bit shocked at how easily it all came together.

In the meantime, I was getting used to the new house and neighborhood. Though it was in a convenient location, and I was familiar with the city, I found myself devising new routes when I went to work and even to the grocery store. I liked doing that.

Ron was noticing new things too. Time after time, when I took him with me on errands and we came to the stop sign at the end of our block, he saw the playground and track at the school across the street and told me it was a good thing there was a school nearby, "so when we have kids, they won't have far to go." In his mind, evidently, we were young and were going to be raising a family.

It was also a great neighborhood for taking walks. Ron was still into not stepping on cracks, which slowed him down to the point that it became frustrating since I was trying to get some exercise. That was when I discovered the value of being across the street from a school with a track. Having been a track star in high school, he saw it as a place to pick up the pace a bit and seemed to walk with great determination. In addition, there were no cracks, so it was double win.

I later discovered there was another advantage. As his pace continued to slow, I found that I could have him walk in one direction then I could walk at a faster pace in the opposite direction, the whole time being able to keep an eye on him.

At the other end of our block there was a park and we walked along the sidewalk when we went there. Not only did Ron make sure not to step on the cracks, but I also quickly learned, thanks to him reading the stamp in the sidewalk every time we passed it, that C. L. Abeyta, was the contractor who did the cement work in our new neighborhood. At first it was funny and something I hadn't even noticed. It certainly was not a company or name with which I was familiar. Eventually I got tired of hearing about that over and over whenever we took a walk, though I did my best not to react and just keep my mouth shut.

As the weather warmed and the days became longer, I took him for a walk one afternoon when I got home from work. We were heading to the park and in doing so, passed a crocus garden, in full bloom. He looked over at the garden as we went by and said, "I'm not going to croc you. You'll have to croc yourselves." I thought that was clever for a mind that was impaired! I still giggle when I pass that garden in the springtime.

I was continually reminded that the Alzheimer's journey contained a wide range of experiences, including some laughs, along with many opportunities to "think outside the box."

Not long after we moved, I woke up one night and Ron wasn't in bed. I found him standing in the doorway of the bathroom across the hall and when I took his hand to help him back to bed, he wouldn't budge. That was one of those times I was glad to have taken the classes offered by the Alzheimer's Association, as I recalled learning that those with the disease can perceive rugs or dark parts of the floor as a hole. I guessed that may have been how Ron was seeing the wooden floor in the hallway, clearly not remembering that he had crossed that area to get to the bathroom a few minutes prior.

Though I had turned the light in the bedroom on when I got up, evidently it still wasn't clear. I jumped up and down on the floor to prove that it would be safe to walk there, but that didn't convince him. I tried gently coaxing him, but that didn't work either. In the meantime, I was getting frustrated because I was losing sleep.

Having come to a place where I could see logic wasn't going to work, I suddenly remembered the song, "Tiptoe through the Tulips," that Tiny Tim sang back in the day. I have no clue how that came to my mind, and I didn't know many of the lyrics beyond, "Tiptoe through the tulips with me." But I asked Ron to imagine a garden in the hall with beautiful tulips and when I started to sing, he joined in, took my hand, and we tiptoed through the imaginary tulips back into the bedroom.

Whew, it worked! When we got to the bedroom, he looked at me with a sigh of relief and said, "That was very clever." Again, how he could be so wise as to say that and recognize what had happened, yet be so confused at the same time, was beyond me. I welcomed it, however, as it turned a potentially challenging time into a lighthearted experience.

In addition to ensuring his safety and contentment, one of the main areas where Ron's caregivers and I became more involved was in helping with his self-care. His inability to do things himself was a process.

Before we moved, I had begun laying his clothes out on the bed so he could get dressed more easily after I found him wandering around upstairs in his underwear one day, confused about what to do next. I made sure to choose clothes that were appropriate for the season, so he would be comfortable. I tried to include him in making choices as best he was able. "Would you like to wear this shirt or this shirt today?"

Showering was another area where his caregivers and I progressively needed to get more involved. At first, he just needed a few reminders. One day when Moira, Ron's ex-daughter-in-law, was watching him, she noticed that he had been in the shower for quite some time, so while standing just outside the bathroom door trying to coach him without interfering too much, she asked him if he had washed his "privates."

Ron replied, "There are only non-commissioned officers in here."

We'll never know if he washed himself thoroughly, but that's another one that gave us some giggles.

When he continued to increase the length of time he spent in the shower, other caregivers discovered that they could go to the basement and turn off the hot water, which brought Ron out in a hurry. And then there were times when we just let him stand in the shower until the water eventually ran cold. As his disease progressed, we got more involved, coaching him to make sure that he soaped then rinsed his entire body. Sometimes he didn't even seem to know where to look for the shampoo, much less remember to use it.

One day when I was preparing to help him with his shower, he stood there fully clothed and said, "I don't know what to do." I was surprised as I would have thought taking off his clothes would come naturally in getting ready to take a shower, after a lifetime habit of doing that. Then there was a period when Ron regularly asked why he had to put deodorant in his armpits. I got tired of having to answer that question over and over and tried approaching it from the physiological perspective, the social perspective, and anything else I could think of—primarily to keep myself entertained, I think.

Above all, the most challenging times when giving him a shower occurred when I would just finish getting him dry and suddenly there would be pee running down his leg. Sometimes when that happened, it took a lot of patience for me not to react with anger or an unhelpful comment, especially if we were on a schedule. It generally required showering his legs again in addition to cleaning up the floor.

Then there was shaving. Ron always liked to use shaving cream and a razor blade and at first, he was still able to manage that by himself. But over time, I noticed small changes such as stopping after he finished shaving without cleaning off the blade or turning off the water, and just staring at himself in the mirror.

His caregivers and I gradually became more involved, just coaching him at first until we eventually had to actually participate in shaving him. At that time, I got an electric shaver and a beard-trimmer because I didn't want to risk cutting him. I then had to get some lessons from the guys in his family on how to use the beard-trimmer.

Several months before I retired when I got home from work one day, Steve told me that Ron was still in bed, and he had only been able to get him up to go to the bathroom once or twice. I went into the bedroom and asked Ron if he felt bad and he said it was his head. When I asked him if he had a headache, he said "No," and looked like he couldn't think of what he wanted to say so I asked if he was referring to his confusion. He said, "Yes."

After Steve left, I went back to see if Ron was ready to get up, and told him, "You must have gotten a lot of sleep since you were in bed all day." He said he wasn't sleeping but just feeling sad and scared because he thought I was gone. It took a long time for me to convince him that I loved him and was going to be there for him.

Finally, when he was ready to get up, I took him outside, thinking that might help change his focus. While I was puttering around the yard Ron started whistling, indicating that he was happy. Yet when we came in, he said, "The neighbors must think I'm crazy. No wonder nobody likes me."

I tried to convince him otherwise, but again it seemed like he was very much in touch with his confusion and his inability to relate to people as he had done in the past. That was a hard day.

It reminded me of another occasion when Ron seemed to be aware of his situation. I had been reading a book called *Dancing on Quicksand*, written by Alzheimer's caregiver Marilyn Mitchell. It was laying on the kitchen counter when he picked it up and became very engrossed in looking at it. I mentioned that it seemed like he found it interesting, and he said, "It's about a guy like me." Then he explained how it made him feel better, knowing that there is someone else who is the way he is, and he even used the word Alzheimer's. Wow!

That Sunday evening when I was helping him get ready for bed, in one of his lucid moments, Ron talked about what a good job I was doing taking care of him, as he had previously done. He said he would not have gotten this far without me, and that he would not do so well if he had to take care of me. When I told him that I would be quitting my job soon so I could be his primary caregiver, he asked what we were going to do for money, saying he wanted me to be sure to take care of myself.

I did my best to explain that I would be getting my retirement income, and that we had his as well. Conversations such as that were treasures, though I had learned they were not significant indicators that he was getting better, as much as I longed for that.

Similarly, a few weeks later, while eating breakfast one Sunday, the conversation turned to Ron's caregivers. I told him that his son Curt, would be moving away so he would no longer be seeing him regularly. Then again, I told him that I would soon be retiring so I would be the primary person to stay with him during the day. He then had a little giggle, became teary-eyed, and said, "Oh good." When I asked him why he thought that would be good, he said, "Because I love you." By that time, we were both teary.

As the date for my retirement approached, I could see that would probably bring a new chapter to our journey. I would be able to stay more focused on the time I spent with Ron and include more activities. Yet, at the same time, I would be with him day after day, night after night. I would need to be sure to include the self-care that I was continually reminded of, even by Ron.

Chapter 10

AS OUR JOURNEY PROGRESSED, I seemed to be stepping more openly and honestly into the variety of experiences that life offers instead of trying to maintain an even keel as I had done much of my life. In addition to facing the challenging times and the losses involved more openly, I was also allowing myself to be touched more deeply by the simple moments of closeness that we sometimes shared. But instead of trying to hold onto those as I did in the past, I was learning that those, too, were part of the ever-changing experience of life, as Ron could be dramatically different the next day... or even the next hour.

I was reminded of that a few days after I retired. A couple up the street in our new neighborhood had invited us to come to their mountain cabin to see the changing aspens and have lunch with them. It was a wonderful, much-needed outing and I was very grateful that they asked us to do that.

While driving home, I checked in with Ron. He said he had a nice time and it appeared that he had been enjoying himself when we were there. As we drove into town, I noticed that the sky behind us was filled with a beautiful red sunset, an experience that we always enjoyed sharing. I patted Ron's leg and told him that I loved him and he said, "Just keep both hands on the wheel."

Later, when I was helping him get into bed, I told him that I really enjoyed our day together and he said, "Well, you didn't act like it." When I tried to get clarification about why he said that, of course he couldn't tell me.

Nevertheless, I felt very sad he would say that when, to me, it seemed like a wonderful outing, our neighbors were kind enough to invite us, and I had retired so I could be with him and make time for such experiences. It gave me second thoughts about my decision to retire and care for him. Thankfully, I didn't entertain them for long and woke up the next morning ready for a new day.

Now that I was on a 24/7 shift caring for Ron, and no longer working, it became easier to stay connected with my friends in the Alzheimer's community. Since they had been full-time caregivers for some time, they were able to provide me with helpful information.

Maria told me about the daytime support group that was offered by the Alzheimer's Association. She also invited me to take Ron to the daycare program that she had found for Doug.

I contacted Bonnie, the woman who ran that, and made arrangements to take Ron and see how he would do. It turned out he seemed to feel comfortable there and fit right in. That was invaluable, as it provided a few hours a couple times a week when I could have time to myself, run errands, or attend the Alzheimer's Association support group. In addition, Bonnie provided numerous social events where we could meet the other spouses who were on the same journey. In fact, after dropping our husbands off, several of the other wives and I often had lunch together.

Understanding that I was not the only one on this crazy journey and hearing the stories of others in the support group helped tremendously. We could call each other when we just needed to vent, with questions about anything with which we were struggling, or sometimes even when we were in tears. Jerry once referred to us as a "tribe." We were in it together.

One night after Ron was in bed, I got a call from Wayne regarding his wife, Gail. The subject of our conversation was managing incontinence of stool, which by that time was a regular occurrence with Ron. He had been wearing Depends for urinary incontinence for quite some time, so when accidents with poop started happening regularly, at least the mess was more manageable and I had already experienced dealing with it.

Gail was about as far along in the disease as Ron was, but she had not been incontinent until recently. The evening we talked Wayne described an accident she had on their living room carpet that day. He said that when he tried to clean her up in the shower, Gail's continuous refusal to let him do that left him feeling like their bathroom was a war zone and he was being held captive amidst the mess.

It was certainly helpful for him to be able to "vent" that night and for me to be reminded that I wasn't the only one dealing with such things. Clearly none of us had done this before and it was good to have contact with others who understood the crazy situations in which we found ourselves.

As I began caring for Ron full-time, I became more and more aware of the opportunities it provided to practice having patience and being present in the moments, whatever they brought. I was grateful for mindfulness which made that easier.

I was reminded of that one day, not long after I retired. It was a crisp autumn morning, and Ron was acting rather unsettled, so I tried to direct him to something he would like to do. He said he wanted to go outside. When he started to go out, I said, after having gone to take some trash out earlier, "It is pretty cool out. Don't you want to put on a jacket?"

He responded, "No," and went out. However, within a minute he was back and said, "It's cold out there."

So, I went to the closet, got a jacket, and helped him put it on. He then went to the door, but said he decided he didn't want to go out, so we took the jacket off. However, within a couple of minutes, he looked out and said he would like to go sit in the sun, so we put the jacket back on. I went out and put a chair in the sunny part of the yard for him. He sat for barely a minute, then got up and began pacing in the yard.

Thankfully, having retired, I felt a little more relaxed about my time and was able to stay with the process exactly as it was playing out.

Yet, as time went on, I was soon to discover that I was not quite so relaxed about other things. When Ron went through the kitchen while walking circles in the house, I often had my back to him as I would be standing at the sink, or sometimes bent over, looking for something in the refrigerator or loading the dishwasher. That seemed to bring out a behavior in him that I had never seen previously in our relationship. He smacked my butt as he walked by.

To him, it may have been intended to be a love pat, however it startled me, and I wasn't expecting it. Because it was not accompanied by any loving words or behavior, and physical intimacy was no longer a part of our lives, it felt very condescending to me. I became aware of wanting to react by kneeing him in the balls, that arose as a result of having previously taken self-defense classes. There were times when I was able to take a deep breath and let it go, but certainly there were other times when my reaction got the best of me, and I yelled at him.

I didn't like feeling ill at ease in my own kitchen. And to top it off, I couldn't ask him not to do that because he wouldn't know what I was talking about, nor would he be able to remember the next time he walked through the kitchen.

After that happened several times, I was reminded again that I was the one who had to change—to adapt. I began squatting instead of bending over, thinking that if I was lower, I wouldn't be such a target.

However, one day when I was looking in the refrigerator for mustard to make him a sandwich, he came by and actually kicked my butt. My "fight" hormones were activated, and I became furious! At first, I yelled as a result of being both startled and mad. Since I couldn't talk to him about it or leave to have some time to myself, the thing that came to mind was to go across the street to the school and walk on the track—in opposite directions. That way I could get away from him and actively move to release some tension, yet still keep an eye on him.

So, after he finished his sandwich, that's where we went. It helped, but I wasn't very friendly to him for the rest of the day and was glad when it was finally time for him to go to bed.

It was interesting, however, the next day when I gave Ron a hug after making a nice breakfast and helping him get settled with his drawing while listening to *Prairie Home Companion*, he said I was mean to him. He went on to say that I put poison in his food and yelled at him. It sounded like my reaction of the previous day still resonated with him. And he even remembered it!

I later learned that while words aren't always understood by Alzheimer's patients, they relate to tone of voice and facial expressions. They evidently feel the emotions of others and retain them, even relating those to that person the next time they see them. Apparently, that's what was happening.

After that incident I could see that I needed to make some adjustments. I either needed to limit my bending and squatting to times when Ron was napping or sitting down or keep an eye out for him and stand up and turn around when I heard him coming. I also needed to continue to practice pausing and taking deep breaths if it occurred. I even surprised myself as I wondered if maybe I should make arrangements for him to live somewhere else.

I wasn't ready for him to live in a facility yet. However, I also recognized the importance of keeping myself safe and minimizing my stress, so I worked with the other options. And interestingly, he began doing it less and eventually stopped.

After I retired, I was also taking Ron with me on errands and had more opportunities to be with him in public. That, too, was a learning experience, and using the public restrooms was probably the biggest challenge.

At first, I let him go into the men's room by himself, though on several occasions had to ask another fellow to see if anyone else was in there so I could go in and get him, as sometimes he forgot to come out.

During that period, when we were on errands and I was in the ladies' room, I tried giving him something to hold onto and asked him to wait outside, thinking he would be less likely to wander.

I laugh when I think about the time I left him waiting with the grocery cart which happened to be next to the ATM machine at the in-store bank. When I finished in the restroom and came out, Ron was not by the cart where I left him but was with a man from the bank who said Ron told him he put a twenty-dollar bill in the ATM and didn't get anything back. When I told the gentleman about Ron's Alzheimer's, he seemed to understand.

However, those and other similar experiences led me to start taking Ron into the ladies' rooms with me and using the handicap stall so both of us could use the toilet. Older women seemed to understand, but we got some looks from the teenagers. I was always glad when family restrooms were available.

One of the most embarrassing experiences in public happened one summer day when I took Ron to Cy's, his favorite hamburger stand. As we were getting out of the car, a man and his wife who was quite overweight, came out with their lunches and sat down at a picnic table. I had to go to the bathroom which had an outside entrance, meaning that we would go by their table to get there.

As we passed them Ron leaned over to the man and said, "It looks like you like fat women." My heart skipped a beat. I couldn't believe what I heard. I planned to stop and apologize when we passed them after I finished in the bathroom, but they no doubt realized that we'd be coming by again and they were gone. That, and a number of other comments he made about the size of women, their breasts and "nice asses," contributed to me trying to run interference in such places as restaurants and the grocery store and eventually even limiting the places where I took Ron.

Thankfully, I seemed to be getting much better at surfing. Due to all the practice, I was meeting each moment more skillfully. In addition, I was learning to have more patience and to be kind to myself when I fell off the surfboard.

I was discovering that the journey with Ron could be aggravating, frustrating, and stressful, as well as fascinating, humorous, tender, and loving. The more I could meet each moment with openness, curiosity, and a willingness to be with whatever was happening, the easier it got. I was becoming very clear about the value of my mindfulness practice.

Interestingly, evidence of Ron's "well-trained higher cognitive function" that the neurologist identified, continued to show up. It appeared at times throughout much of his journey until the late stage. One day in talking to him, I compared two things and said one was the "best."

He corrected me saying, "Don't you know when comparing more than two things you use best? When you're only talking about two things, you should use better." Of course, why didn't I remember that?

On another occasion he came into the kitchen one morning and said something about it being Saturday. I said, "Actually it's Tuesday." Then he looked outside and saw the shadow of the roof of our house on the fence. He said, "It's 'Tober.' I can tell by the sun." Indeed, the sun was getting lower in the sky, and I was shocked that he could evidently see that, even in a place where he had not even lived prior to Alzheimer's. It was in fact, October.

The day he asked me why x-rays are called "Roentgen," I almost dismissed it, thinking that he had made that up like some of the invented words I would occasionally hear him say. However, I Googled it and was amazed to find that it referred to a German physicist who discovered x-rays. Ron then said, "They talk a lot about him in class," evidently remembering something from dental school.

His brain was fascinating! That demonstrated something I had learned about Alzheimer's patients. It's easier for them to remember things from the past than something that is current.

The giggles and humorous moments that Ron unknowingly offered definitely made the journey a bit easier and helped relieve the stress of having a husband who was no longer competent.

One day while I was working at my desk, he was looking at the books in my study and saw, *Where the Mind Meets the Body* by Harris Dienstfrey. He said, "That must be a book about the neck."

Another time when I said to him, "It looks like you need to blow your nose," and handed him a tissue, he ignored the tissue, stuck out his lower lip, and blew upward toward his nose. I realized that I needed to hold the tissue on his nose and give him more specific instructions.

I also got a chuckle the day I was trimming his beard for him, and he said, "The General will be mad about this." When I asked him why, he said, "Because we're supposed to be tough and do things for ourselves."

I got a chance to practice what I had been learning about being selective in taking what he said seriously, one day when he was walking around the circle in the house. I commented that it looked like he enjoyed doing that and he said he liked doing it because, "It gives me time to think about all the nasty things you do to me."

But the next day, it was a different story. The song, "I Don't Know Why I Love you Like I Do" was being played on *Prairie Home Companion* while he walked. When he came into the kitchen, he was crying hard and grabbed me and hugged me. Interestingly, a couple days later, he was singing that same song without being prompted by hearing it elsewhere and hugged me again. If I had still been angry about him saying that I did nasty things to him, I would have missed those loving moments.

The tender side of Ron made other appearances as well. One day when we were getting ready to go somewhere, I told him that I still had to put on my lipstick. He replied, "Don't worry. You're beautiful just as you are." Rarely had he said such sweet things. He usually expressed that part of himself through his poetry.

I also saw a simple, tender side of Ron during the holiday season that year, as he'd start crying whenever he heard Christmas music; even when they were playing "Rudolph the Red Nosed Reindeer" over the speaker in the grocery store.

Other special times with Ron occurred just in the process of doing life. One September day, I was working in the yard and asked him to hold the shovel for me, having learned that it was easier to give him a simple task rather than have him wander aimlessly. In the meantime, he started to dig in an area where I had not yet planted anything, and he dug for about a half hour. After doing that, he picked up the end of the hose and without turning on the water, walked around the yard for quite a while just carrying it, eventually sitting on a bench in the sunshine.

When it started to cool off, I invited him to come inside while I finished getting dinner. As he came in, he saw his drawing tablet on the dining room table and sat down to draw without any coaching from me. That was unusual. That evening, when I was helping him get ready for bed, he was whistling. Clearly, he was happy and at peace.

Though that day had gotten off to a rough start due to Ron peeing on the floor in front of the toilet then tracking it all over the house which I had to clean up, I was grateful for the way it turned out. I would have loved to hear him whistle at the end of every day, but I had long since learned to let go of such expectations. Anything could happen and it often didn't seem to be related to anything I had done—or not done. However, I knew that the more present and relaxed I was, the higher the likelihood that Ron would have a good day.

One day I had an experience where I saw how much he was aware of my state of mind. While he was brushing his teeth, I was standing next to him and started looking at a place on my arm where I had gotten poked by the rose bush while cutting the lawn. He casually looked over and said, "You're not paying attention to me."

That brought me back! No being distracted when I was helping him! Then there was the day when Ron was eating some fruit and dropped a blueberry. He said, "Cyndy, could you please pick that up for me?" just like normal. And the day I took him with me to the grocery store for a couple of items and got ice cream first, he commented that we should get that last so it wouldn't melt before we were finished. I was amazed!

The occasional shifts from Alzheimer's to what seemed to be "normal" were baffling. But by this time we were about five years into the journey and I felt like I was finally understanding that didn't mean that Ron was going to get better. Nor did I try to hold onto those experiences. They were simply passing phases to be enjoyed while they were occurring.

One evening Moira was watching him while I attended a class on financial management after retirement. When I got home, she greeted me saying, "You're not going to believe this," and immediately took me to the table where Ron had been sitting.

There, in his drawing pad, was a profile of an oddly shaped face. The color was light green and the features were grotesque with an abstract quality. Beneath each large, out-of-proportion nostril, was a long drip. The ear was pierced with a hoop, there was a large oblong turquoise eye, one sprig of curly hair on top of the head, and something around the neck that resembled a leather collar with studs. Toward the bottom of the page the word "me" was printed with an arrow pointing toward the picture, and above, in a cartoon-like cloud, Ron printed, "I AM THE MOST HANDSOME MAN IN THIS STATE OF C~~OLORADO~~ !!!!!!!!!!!" However, above where he had crossed out all but the letter "C" in Colorado, he wrote *CONFUSION*.

I looked at Moira wide-eyed. He didn't know his address or what the date was. He thought Kennedy was president. Yet, along with some of the other moments of clarity to which I referred he was apparently able to identify that he was in a state of confusion. It was fascinating to see how he tried to make sense of what he was experiencing.

Chapter 11

EVIDENTLY, WHAT I WAS LEARNING about being the one who had to change and managing myself while caring for Ron, was apparent to others. Our friend Clark, who was in Ron's poetry group, frequently came to hang out with Ron, usually bringing a lemon meringue pie which Ron loved.

One day, after coming over to visit, he sent me an email in which he said, "You have everyone's respect and admiration for your enormous kindness and patience in dealing with Ron. Having been on the edge of needing homecare recently, I realize what it takes."

And in a conversation with Moira, she referred to the way I treated Ron as being "honoring."

In seeing it that way, I felt like maybe I was getting myself out of the way so I wasn't reacting so personally to what was occurring, but just responding as best I could to whatever was going on for him.

By far the most touching comments I received were in an email from Sara, his daughter who lived out of state. In it, she recognized that not only did I have to care for her dad one hundred percent of the time, but I also had to manage our lives and do everything by myself (unlike having a partner to help with things, as he used to do).

It felt good to have that acknowledged, especially by someone in Ron's family. She went on to say how grateful she was because she didn't have to worry about her dad's care and safety since I was looking after him with "such sweet love and mindfulness." She then closed saying, "That gives me such a sense of peace in my heart."

Caring for Ron continued to help me see that many of the things I used to think were important were not, and were cultural programming that I bought into, especially as a woman.

I could relate to the words of Deborah Eden Tull, when she said, "Society teaches us to follow a script for behavior, rather be in touch with our own unique essence and express that essence fully."[1]

Having started the Alzheimer's journey with the belief that I had to get our lives back under control, do it right, and look good, I was beginning to see that it was more important to be able to be present to whatever was happening. So the kind words that others shared, fit for me as an acknowledgement of my love for Ron versus proof that I was doing it right. And as his disease progressed, I got to practice being with many things that I could not have even imagined earlier in our relationship.

One of the changes that became apparent as Ron declined was his tiredness. He often slept over ten hours at night and had afternoon naps of up to two hours. In addition, he sometimes fell asleep while he was drawing as well as when he was at daycare.

In eating, he would often lose interest after a couple of bites, and I would have to put the fork back into his hand to remind him to continue. Overall, he seemed more withdrawn and less responsive. At times it was hard to get his attention to ask him something or remind him to come eat.

I also noticed that he did not move as easily. Not only had his walking slowed, but he was more slumped. And he did not change positions at night when he was sleeping. In general, I referred to what I saw during that period as Ron becoming "paralyzed." As those changes became more apparent, there were times when I would be caring for him with tears in my eyes. The losses from day to day throughout the course of the disease were very sad to watch. I was glad I was willing to let those feelings be there and feel them instead of denying them and having them show up later with anger toward Ron, or eventually affect my own health.

Because it was increasingly difficult to have normal conversations, occasionally I started singing to find a way to connect to him.

One day, I started singing the old song, "I Love You a Bushel and a Peck." When I got to the part about a "hug around the neck," I realized I didn't know the rest of the words. When I paused, Ron picked up with, ". . . and a barrel and a heap and I'm talking in my sleep about you." Really?

I Googled it and guess what? He was right. From then on, when I sang that, I paused and Ron pitched in with his part. It soon became a regular part of our routine. I found that very touching, especially since we were unable to connect through our conversations as we had done in the past. Now, we had a song to sing together.

Clearly, his Alzheimer's was affecting every aspect of our relationship including our roles and responsibilities and our finances, as well as our communication and how we spent our time. The intimacy we shared in our relationship had changed, as well. During the few years prior to determining that Ron had Alzheimer's, sex had not been particularly satisfying for either of us. We were getting old. Ron frequently experienced erectile dysfunction and I had developed vaginal dryness after going through menopause.

When our relationship changed due to his Alzheimer's, I no longer felt physically attracted to him. In fact, in the early stages of the bitch, I didn't want him to touch me. He felt like a stranger. I never really missed our physical relationship, as I had so many other things to focus on with caring for him, especially while I was working.

Then, as I transitioned to becoming his full-time care partner, I noticed that the love I was feeling for him was different—not romantic but more like a mother caring for her child. I still didn't have sexual feelings toward him.

But one night I was surprised. When I was checking on Ron before I went to bed to make sure his Depends didn't need to be changed, I noticed that he had taken them off and had an erection. It turned out he was awake and made a comment about wanting me. He asked me if I was coming to bed, and I could tell he wanted to make love. In that moment I could feel myself wanting the closeness that had long been missing from our relationship, but what about his cleanliness due to the incontinence? And what about my responsibility? My role now was to care for him and make sure he was safe.

As a result of some combination of loving him, missing our closeness, and curiosity, I gave him several of the moist wipes we used in the bathroom, and helped him clean his hands, penis and pubic area. Then I took off my clothes and crawled into bed with him. For a few minutes being close felt good—it had been so long.

However, it soon became clear that we weren't going to be able to have intercourse, which was not surprising. Ron then started masturbating, so I did the same and we each had an orgasm. Despite the way it played out, it still felt like a tender time of loving and intimacy.

From the standpoint of being Ron's care partner, I found myself feeling very happy that he was able to have that experience. I liked it when he was happy. It had also been pleasurable for me, and for a few minutes, in my mind, he was more like the Ron I used to know. And yet, at the same time, it also seemed to have an almost incestuous quality. My identity was in a kind of hazy zone, like I had shifted roles for a little while. Who was I?

After I got up, I got a new pair of Depends for Ron, helped him put them on, and that was that. I was his care partner again, but what about his wife? It was a one-time thing. I didn't encourage that again, and Ron didn't remember.

When I got into bed a little later, he was already asleep. I found myself in my usual spot as far away from him as I could get. Since he had become incontinent, having a large bed was helpful so I could avoid getting too close to him as by morning, the Depends were often saturated and had leaked. Though I had water-resistant pads on the bed, I still found myself changing the sheets frequently. I was getting tired of that.

One weekend in browsing through Craigslist, I saw an ad for a medical bed. I took Ron out to look at it. Suddenly I recognized that sleeping in separate beds was a big step and I wasn't ready yet, so we went home without purchasing it.

However, a couple of months later after changing the king-sized bed numerous times one week, I decided it was time to look into separate beds again. I checked on Craigslist and found a hospital bed at a reasonable price as well as a twin captain's bed with drawers underneath. Getting that would not only provide a place for me to sleep. It would also give me a place where I could store some of the supplies and bedding for Ron.

I was rather surprised at myself in how quickly I moved this time. I took Ron and we went to the two locations to check out the beds. I purchased each of them on the spot, then came home and talked to our neighbor about helping me bring them home in his truck. He was kind to take the time, as picking them up required two different trips. After putting them in the garage, I left them there for several weeks until I could arrange for someone to help me take out the old bed and bring in the new ones. Looking back, I realize that keeping them in the garage also gave me more time to get used to the idea of sleeping separately.

The next time I went to my support group I shared about having done that and one of the other participants said when the time came for her to get separate beds for her and her husband, it was a "defining moment" as she suddenly felt like her role changed from wife to nurse.

I could relate. Though I had been caring for Ron for quite some time and my role had obviously changed during that time, I could still sense the loss that came with that shift as it meant we would no longer be sleeping together. It felt like our husband-and-wife roles were now definitely gone. It also seemed significant in that it was another step in me looking out for my own needs as well as being more independent. It was clear that I was gradually becoming a different person, as was Ron.

In that period of the progression of Ron's disease, I also noticed that he periodically expressed what appeared to be fear. I could understand. If I were in his situation and had an inkling of how confused I was, I would definitely feel afraid. He could no longer access the things he had used to feel comfortable and make sense out of his life. Having initially experienced his illness as a disruption to the "reality" upon which I had based my life where I felt like I had some control and certainty, I could understand. But I had a functioning brain, and with time, I began to see it differently.

I remember early one morning when I helped Ron go to the bathroom, after we had the separate beds in place. I changed his Depends while he was sitting on the toilet and was ready to help him go back to bed, but he was hesitant to stand up. When I asked him what the problem was, he said he needed to get up the courage. Finally, with a little more encouragement and physical support from me, he stood up and walked to bed, holding my hand. When I helped him lie down, I could see that he was still afraid so I squeezed into the bed and laid down so I could hug him. Eliot then got on top of him, purring. A few minutes later Ron said he felt better, and he soon dozed off.

On another occasion, one morning when Ron woke up, I kissed him on the cheek. In response he said, "I'm glad I can still feel that." When I asked him if there some things he couldn't feel, he said, "Yes, because I'm dead."

Again, I felt very sad. I could imagine how he might feel that way as he had lost so many of the abilities and experiences that he used to enjoy. In fact, I remembered reading something about an Alzheimer's patient referring to himself as being dead. I just stayed with Ron and loved him, honoring his feeling.

I also started noticing that he periodically clenched the last three fingers of his left hand in a fist. I was concerned as it seemed like in doing that, he would be apt to lose his flexibility, so I started to open his hand and massage that area when I could. When I asked him why he did that he said, "It gives me something to control."

Similarly, one day when I was helping him get up from his nap, he had unbuckled his belt and was holding onto it. When I asked what he was doing, he said, "It makes me feel safe." And during the same period, there were also times when he was in the bathroom, that he asked me not to leave him alone, saying, "Don't go."

One of the big events of our journey also occurred during that same period, apparently due to him being agitated. For some time, I had been noticing his restlessness when I turned on the evening news which we usually watched together, so I no longer did that. However, that evening, Hurricane Sandy was bearing down on the New York coastline so I turned it on as my nephew and his family lived in Brooklyn and I wanted to see how it might be affecting them. At the same time, a fellow showed up to aerate the yard and began going around the front and back yard with his aerator. Simultaneously, there was some commotion across the street as the elderly gentleman who lived there had just passed away. His children and grandchildren were gathering at his house bringing more cars and people to the area than we typically saw. Needless to say, there was a lot going on.

When the fellow finished aerating, I was taking a check out to pay him and as I walked toward the front door, I noticed Ron was walking behind me. When I turned around and looked at him, he had unzipped his pants and had his penis in his hand. Since the man outside was waiting for me to bring him the check, I minimized my interaction with Ron, telling him to go to the bathroom if he needed to and otherwise to put his penis back in his pants and zip them up. Then I went out, locking the door behind me. I was focused on what I thought needed to be done right then and couldn't be bothered by Ron.

I was outside for a maximum of five minutes, talking to the fellow about when to next aerate our yard. When I came inside, I saw Ron in the TV room with the butane lighter from my office in his hand. I used it occasionally to light a candle when I was meditating. He was flicking it on and off but allowed me to take it from him without a fuss. However, I then began to notice the smell of something burning. I felt a wave of panic move through me. I looked first in the kitchen, then realized he had been in my study to get the lighter, so I went there. I was shocked when I saw that the pile of newspaper articles I had collected to help me decide who to vote for in the coming election, was on fire. And it was on a wooden credenza that was only a short distance from my computer.

Clearly that triggered my fight, flight, or freeze reaction. I remember shaking and feeling beside myself. The fire didn't seem big enough to report it and flee or get out of the house without at least trying to put it out. So, in this case, I ended up "fighting" and began to take immediate action to extinguish the flames. I didn't pause or even recall thinking of what to do, but thankfully, something I had previously seen on Facebook came to mind. That was a reminder about what to do if something you're cooking in a pot on the stove catches fire. In such a case, it showed covering the pot with a wet towel, after turning off the heat underneath.

There was a bathroom next to my office, so I went in and immediately took a bath towel off the rack and put it in the basin, saturating it with water. In the back of my mind, I thought I might ruin the towel doing that, but so what? I needed to get the fire out! I totally forgot that I had a fire extinguisher in the kitchen. Anyway, the bathroom was closer, and I didn't need to read any instructions to get a towel wet.

As I put the towel on the pile of burning newspaper, the flames subsided. But a small piece of blackened paper which was still burning, separated from the rest of the paper and went behind the credenza. Wasting no time, I went back into the bathroom and got another wet towel. I might have to buy a whole set of new towels—no problem. I put that towel behind the credenza and watched as the flames died.

Slowly, I picked up each towel to make sure the fire was completely extinguished. Whew. But I was still keeping an eye on the small pieces of blackened paper that seemed to have floated all over the room.

I could feel the tension. And then the fire alarm associated with my security system started to blare. It apparently took a couple of minutes for the smoke to activate that. As I was standing there looking for little flare-ups, the alarm company called to check and see if they needed to send the fire truck.

After telling the caller it appeared I had put out the fire, I noticed that I felt weak and was trembling. I needed someone to be with me. I called Aleah to see if she could come over, and thankfully, she had just gotten off work. I didn't take time to check on Ron and was glad that he stayed away from the area and had no way to get out of the house since the doors were locked. I stood, looking at the small black burned pieces of paper all over my office and finally got out the vacuum. What else to do?

When Aleah arrived, I was well into cleaning up the mess. She helped, pulling out furniture and pointing out areas where I had missed. I was grateful, as it could have been so much worse.

As she was getting ready to leave, she said, "So Mom, what else could Ron get into that you should put away?" My mind immediately went to the kitchen knives that were on a magnetic strip beside the sink. I would put those in a drawer.

I had not seen any signs that Ron was one to go around opening cupboards and drawers like others I heard about in my support group, at least not yet. But it had become very clear that I had to stay alert and assess situations more closely out of concern about what could happen.

I then breathed a sigh of relief and went to find Ron so I could get us something for dinner. I was glad to have kept my wits about me, so I didn't get upset with him for starting the fire. I acted like nothing happened. He was drawing. Luckily, he found something to do that would calm him during that time.

The next day when he woke up from his nap, I found Ron with the blanket all bunched up in his hand and wrapped around his head. I asked him if I could straighten it out, but he told me he wanted it that way because it made him feel safe. I understood. I was slowly learning that in each situation that arose, I also wanted to feel safe. Yet, I was learning that relying on something or someone outside of myself to provide those things was not a healthy way to live. It was up to me.

When I washed the towels, I was amazed to find they had not been damaged. I hung them back in the bathroom, feeling very grateful to have learned about using towels to put out a fire. I then checked to make sure that I put the butane lighter in the closet.

I learned two lessons with that experience. 1) If I ever see Ron agitated like he was when I was going out to pay the fellow who did the aerating, my focus needs to be on him first. Everything else can wait. And 2) Just as I was learning not to blame Ron for his actions and to have compassion for him, I needed to apply that to myself as well. After the fire I could hear the tape in my head saying, "You should have known better."

But when I looked at it from another perspective, I knew I was doing my best and simply overlooked the potential danger in having the lighter in a place where Ron could find it, especially since he rarely went into my study. It served no purpose to be angry at myself. I needed to have compassion for both of us.

Chapter 12

WHEN I READ AN ARTICLE that pointed out, "No sooner has the caregiver grappled with one set of problems, when the patient's further deterioration creates new and more intractable ones,"[1] I could relate. If there was one thing that was consistent about caring for Ron, it was that.

I had learned in my reading and heard from others in my support group, that when the symptoms of an Alzheimer's patient seem to worsen rather rapidly, that could mean that they have an infection of some sort—often a urinary tract infection (UTI).

So, one day in December, when I witnessed Ron's decline suddenly becoming more pronounced, I was on alert. In particular, he seemed more tired, and his walking was slower with an overall lack of stability. In addition, he did not respond to verbal direction or cues as he usually did.

When I took his temperature, it was not elevated. I took him to the doctor's office where they took blood to run labs, and with much patience, we were able to get Ron to pee a little bit in a cup. The urine sample was still in the normal range, so I was advised to keep an eye on him. They suggested that I see if I could get him to drink more water and return if his symptoms worsened. In the meantime, they said they would call me if the lab results showed any other symptoms.

Over the next couple of weeks during the holidays, Ron's symptoms fluctuated, and he actually seemed better at times. We went to his granddaughter Beth's house for a family get-together, and I had my family over for a holiday celebration as well.

However, one day in early January he was really sleepy and stayed in bed until late afternoon. Because he had not walked much that day, I suggested he get a little bit of exercise by walking around the circle in the house. I gave him the walker because he seemed a bit unstable. I was working in the kitchen and noticed that even with the walker he did not seem very steady, so the next time he came through the kitchen I was going to help him sit down. Before I could do that, however, I heard a thud in the living room and found him on the floor. He did not appear to be injured but I could see that I wasn't going to be able to get him up.

I called 911. Soon the paramedics arrived and after they examined Ron, they felt that he should get checked out in the ER. At first, I was really upset with myself about not supervising him enough to keep him from falling. But after seeing the workup they did in the ER which determined that he had a UTI, I was glad that he was there. If I had stopped his walking sooner so he could sit down and rest, who knows how much worse he would have gotten before we figured out what was wrong.

He got his first dose of the antibiotic via IV while still in the ER. The doctor suggested we admit him as he wasn't sure I could care for him, but I convinced him I'd been doing it for a long time and that I had help, so they let me bring him home. We had a bowl of soup when we got home, and I called to see if Caleb could come spend the night. Thankfully, he was available. The next morning it was apparent that Ron was already feeling better and as the days went on, he continued to improve.

I noticed feeling fearful and uncertain about what might happen in the future. As I became more aware of my thoughts and emotions, I was able step back, and see it from a more neutral perspective. I found that the experience with the UTI served as a good wakeup call and reminded me to become more familiar with the symptoms and challenges that could possibly arise as Ron's decline continued.

The adjustments that would be needed in his physical environment were becoming more obvious, as were the changes that would be needed in my care interventions. Moving us to a one-story house and getting Ron a medical bed were just the beginning. He was no doubt going to become more immobile in all his movements, including sitting down and standing up, in addition to getting into and out of the bed as well as the car. The pace of his walking would continue to slow to a shuffle, and he would not be as steady on his feet.

I realized that not only did I need to continue to figure things out to meet the ongoing changes, but I was also getting good practice in my ability to be present. I found that being familiar with what I was feeling helped me be more intuitive about what was going on with Ron, so I could meet his needs more skillfully.

In order to prepare for what was to come, one of the things I did was have Steve lower the kitchen table. It was high, and Ron began having trouble getting on the stools we were using. It was easier for me to help him sit on a normal chair and then scoot the chair up to the table.

And, likewise, even though the toilet was one of the higher ones, he needed a place where he could push with his hands to help him stand up or to raise himself so we could wipe him.

Being one who likes to shop at re-sale stores, I found a place where they sold medical equipment that had been used. There I came across the perfect item for toileting. It was a bedside commode with arms on the sides, that had a toilet-like lid and when the bucket was not attached underneath, it could be placed on the floor straddling the toilet and used as a toilet raiser. When the lid was down, it could also be used as a bench.

I continued to look ahead to what else may be next. The shower stall was enlarged when I had the bathroom remodeled shortly after I retired, but I didn't have the door to the hallway widened. However, that would be necessary if Ron were to need a wheelchair. I started talking to friends who helped me look at options. Someone suggested that I could actually remove part of the closet, then have the bathroom door open directly into our bedroom, widening it at the same time. I realized that would even add value to the house as it would then create a "master with an attached bath," as I frequently saw advertised in real estate listings.

I called Chris to get an estimate. He said it would take a couple of weeks, during which the bedroom would be torn up. I knew that I couldn't manage Ron at home during that time. In fact, I would have to move to the bedroom in the basement myself. We then scheduled a time for the project, and I made arrangements for Ron to go to respite care.

When the day came, I took him to the same facility I had used previously then went home and rushed to take the clothes out of my closet and removed what I could from the bedroom and bathroom.

The next day the crew covered the areas that were not involved in the construction with plastic and the dust began to fly. I was getting pretty good at adapting despite what was going on, so I worked around the mess.

That afternoon, I got a call from the facility telling me that Ron fell on his face and broke his glasses. He had been taken to the ER due to having a big bump on his head and I could go meet him there. They did not send any staff with him. What a disaster that would have been had I not been available.

Throughout my days as a Patient Representative, I had seen the problems that could arise when a person with dementia did not have someone to represent them when they came to the hospital.

When I arrived with the medical power of attorney in hand, I explained to the staff that Ron had the bump on his forehead as long as I had known him and even he didn't know how he got it. I could tell he wasn't injured otherwise, and I told the nurse he had been brought there unnecessarily based on that bump on his head. She did what was needed so he could be discharged, and I signed the papers.

I then drove him back to the facility and went home to get an old pair of glasses for him. The frame from the broken ones could still be used so the next day I took them to the optical shop to get new lenses.

One evening a couple of days later, I was talking to a friend on the phone when I could see that I was receiving another call from the facility, so I told her I had to go. When I answered they told me that Ron had fallen again. This time he was in route to the hospital in an ambulance, so I drove over to meet him there. After a thorough examination by the physician, including a urinalysis, no medical issues were identified. Again, I drove him back to the facility.

A few more days went by and just as I was starting to get ready for bed one evening, I received another call telling me that Ron had fallen. They had called the paramedics, but Ron was still there and had not yet been transported. I told them I didn't want him to go to the ER. I felt that he didn't need to be traumatized by that experience again and I didn't need another bill for the ER and the related transport. They said I would have to come over to sign a waiver if I didn't want him to go to the hospital. So instead of getting ready for bed, I got in the car.

When I arrived, the ambulance was parked in the driveway, waiting. I went in and they had Ron sitting in a chair. I checked him out and discussed his fall with one of the nurses, then decided I would grant permission for him to stay there. I was glad I kept the Medical Power of Attorney in the glove box of my car. It was coming in handy.

I proceeded to help get Ron ready for bed and stayed with him until he fell asleep. I was questioning myself in making the decisions not to have him checked by a doctor. What if he really was injured? But I knew I could always get him treated. I called to check on him the next day and they didn't see any further evidence of an injury. I was glad that I had been available as there were times when I left town while Ron was in respite.

That weekend I went to visit Ron and found him in the community room where a movie was on the TV. It was the first time he looked like an Alzheimer's patient to me.

He had a few days of growth in his beard, and he was staring with his mouth hanging open, drooling. He didn't even seem to recognize me. It broke my heart to see him that way. I left with tears in my eyes, and by the time I got in the car, I was sobbing.

A few days later the bathroom project was finished. I hurried to get things put away, then late that Friday afternoon, I headed out to pick Ron up and bring him home. He was in a wheelchair when I arrived, looking much the same as he did the day I visited him. The nurse helped me put him in the car, then I could feel the fear set in. What was I going to do when I got home? I didn't have a wheelchair. I wasn't going to be able to get him in the house. I called Aleah and her husband, Jim, to see if they could meet me there.

They had just gotten off work and were at the house by the time I pulled into the driveway. It took the three of us to help Ron out of the car, partially carry him into the house, and put him in bed. Thankfully, Jim had been available.

I found some ice cream in the freezer and put some in a dish that they could feed to Ron while I dashed to the nearby Walgreens to get a "transport chair." The manager was kind enough to give me the one they had on display when I explained that I didn't have time to put one together. I folded it and put it in the back of my car then hurried home. The smaller size and manageability were one of the advantages of that type of chair. It was interesting that I needed to use the new bathroom set-up to accommodate a wheelchair immediately after having the work completed.

I contacted Caleb and he said he could come spend the night to help me with his grandpa if needed. Amazingly, the night was uneventful. Ron must have been exhausted. I was too.

I also contacted Tom that evening. He said he was available to come the next day and help me with his dad over the weekend. We decided to take advantage of the Saturday hours at the doctor's office and have them check Ron out due to the recent falls.

It took me and Tom a considerable amount of time and effort to get Ron up, shower and dress him, feed him, get a urine sample, and help him into the car. The new wheelchair was already coming in handy. The nurse practitioner who treated Ron didn't see any evidence of a UTI nor could she find any reason why he was so weak, slumped over, and having a hard time moving, but she wrote an order for him to have a few visits at home from a physical therapist to see if that would help.

When we got home, Tom suggested that though there were no obvious injuries, the falls probably traumatized his dad to some degree, and perhaps even gave him some sore muscles. That made a lot of sense.

The next day I made Ron's favorite meatloaf and a few other foods he liked, including mashed potatoes, to see if that would help him gain some weight and get his strength back. Tom also urged me to take care of myself and offered his understanding of the need to have his dad live in a facility at some point. But after this recent respite stay, I could see my hesitancy to take that step.

We began discussing what I might do to get help more regularly so Ron could stay home a bit longer. Tom said he thought Caleb, Curt's son, might be looking for a place to live, as he was going to school at the local university.

I called Caleb and he said he would be interested. Having already helped me with his grandpa on several occasions, he had a pretty good idea of what he was getting into. Within a week, we had a plan. He was going to live in the guest room in the basement area at no charge, with the understanding that he would help with Papa about eight hours a week, including both when I was at home and when I was away

In the meantime, I got a "shower chair" so we could make sure Ron was safe when we were showering him. Then, I made arrangements for the physical therapist to come to the house.

At his first visit, he suggested some exercises I could do with Ron so he could become stronger and hopefully have more mobility again. Ron's attention span was limited, so I tried playing some of his favorite music and turning the exercises into a way of dancing together. I also took him outside to walk, as that had been an important part of his exercise, previously.

Initially, I had him use a walker and he was only able to walk about three houses away and back. But within a week, he walked around the block with me without using the walker. It felt like he had recovered physically to the point where he was prior to the respite stay.

With all that had been going on, Ron still had moments when he was aware of his situation. One morning shortly after he woke up, he said he felt sad "because it isn't like it used to be."

I told him I understood. I felt that too. Then I told him, "But everybody still loves you." He seemed to like that. However, as the day went on, I could see that mentally he was not back to where he had been prior to going to the facility.

Per the Alzheimer's Association guidelines, it seemed like Ron's symptoms were entering the Late Stage. He was incontinent of bowel and bladder and had needed round-the-clock assistance with daily activities and personal care for a long time. But now he was sleeping more and his physical abilities such as walking were becoming compromised. I was also beginning to see changes in his ability to eat and chew, especially dense meats.

Though he had previously helped on occasion, after moving in, Caleb discovered that there were many things to become familiar with in caring for his grandpa. In addition, he was learning that there were many aspects of interacting with Papa that could be tricky—often made up on the spot to avert a difficult situation or simply honor Ron, just as he was in that moment.

I'll always remember the time I had gone to have lunch with a friend while Caleb watched Ron. He said Papa told him, "Today I'm getting married," so Caleb went to the trouble to help him get dressed in a shirt, tie, and suit. But then Ron got tired and laid down. Soon he fell asleep. When he woke up, he had apparently forgotten all about the wedding, though he was still dressed in his nice clothes. Caleb was learning that whatever happened was all in a day's experience. That included the importance of the caregiver being able to be flexible and let go of expectations.

In following up on the conversation I had with Tom about taking care of myself, I started getting more help with the other things I had been doing. Since Caleb was helping with Ron, I got Steve to help in the yard as well as clean out the garage, and I had the girl who lived up the street come help me with housecleaning.

In the past, I would have been hesitant to spend money on the things I could do myself, but I was beginning to see it differently. In learning that having Ron live in a facility would cost close to $7,000 a month, I saw that the projects for which I could hire someone to help me, was money well spent. It was an investment in my own well-being so that I would be able to continue to care for Ron.

Another change in caring for Ron that I made during this period was keeping track of his bowel movements, especially now that both Caleb and I were looking after him. Prior to this, he had gotten constipated once, so I gave him a laxative. The resulting mess served as a reminder for me to do my best to keep that from happening again.

On occasion and with some direction, Ron still used the toilet for bowel movements. We then developed a way to track them on a calendar in the bathroom. Based on that, we could modify the "intake" if necessary, to keep him regular, by giving him a mild stool softener and making sure he drank enough water. If nothing more, that gave us something concrete to which to refer in the otherwise ambiguous world in which we were living, though it did seem to help.

It was also becoming necessary to adapt some of the food we were giving Ron, due to the tendency to stuff his mouth full until he couldn't chew or swallow and his increasing difficulty in chewing dense meats. In some of my classes, I had heard the term "mechanical soft" used in reference to an Alzheimer's diet, so I understood that as the loved one changed, their diet might change as well.

The meatloaf worked well for Ron, as did the mashed potatoes. Over the years we had gotten away from casseroles, but I also found myself experimenting with those again. Many things could be mixed with rice, beans, pasta, and baked salmon, canned tuna, or even shredded chicken, to become a good meal. In addition, we sometimes had to pace Ron's eating by moving his plate away from him until he completely chewed and swallowed his last bite.

Yet, in spite of the changes that I continued to make in our environment and in myself, I saw that I needed to address what I had been avoiding. What if the time came when I could no longer safely care for Ron? He was clearly going to continue to decline. Even doing my best, I couldn't prevent that.

Chapter 13

I WAS BECOMING FAMILIAR WITH the various facilities that were available for those needing memory care, some of which I had used during Ron's respite stays. In my involvement with the Alzheimer's Association and hearing from folks in my support group, I understood that many memory care facilities only care for the patients up to a point, but when medical or mobility issues arose, or the patient needed to be fed, those things had to be managed by hospice or even private homecare providers who would come to the facility.

There were also skilled nursing facilities (SNF), but often the staff at those were not adequately trained for managing Alzheimer's patients. In fact, those facilities are frequently used for medical patients who are being discharged from an inpatient hospital stay and need additional, less acute care before they are able to go home. Maria had recently placed Doug in one of those and she spent all day every day there to ensure he was getting the care he needed, as they were not very familiar with providing Alzheimer's care.

However, the place where Curt and I had visited early in Ron's disease was a SNF, as well. It was called Namaste and was devoted to caring only for those with Alzheimer's.

We learned that they had four areas for residents, based on their ability to function. It was also located at the base of Cheyenne Mountain which had a special meaning to Ron from his early days in Colorado Springs. In addition, Namaste was surrounded by nature and had a pond just outside the front door. I realized that honoring Ron's love of nature would be important, even as he declined. As his disease progressed, I visited again and got more information. I learned they had a waiting list.

Since I wanted to keep Ron at home as long as possible, I hoped I could care for him at least until he would qualify for the late-stage unit at Namaste. The residents in that area were generally no longer mobile. I picked up the paperwork so I could complete it and put Ron on their waiting list. It felt like a big step. I kept hearing the words of my mother, "It's better to be safe than sorry"—a message that at times in my life I should have taken seriously and at other times had not been helpful at all, but this time it made sense.

I completed all the paperwork for Namaste and got a physician letter from Dr. Crandall. Then, one summer day, I took Ron with me to deliver the packet. While we were there, we sat for a little while on a bench overlooking the pond and the mountain. When we left, Ron was whistling up a storm! I couldn't have gotten a better indication that it was a good choice. I felt relieved.

As we were driving home, we passed Cy's, the hamburger stand where Ron had commented to the gentleman about his "fat" wife. I decided to give it another try as he enjoyed eating there so much. The place is old and small and before getting to the counter to order our hamburgers, we had to stand in line in the center aisle between rows of tables. While we were waiting there, Ron suddenly asked an older gentleman who was eating at a table with his friends, if he could try his French fries.

At least he asked! The man was very kind and let him take them from his plate. Thankfully, he seemed to understand when I explained to him that Ron had Alzheimer's.

After ordering our lunch, I noticed how hard it was to get Ron to sit down in a booth so we could eat. At the end of our meal, it was even harder to get him to stand up. In fact, in seeing the difficulty I was having, several young men who were eating at another table, stepped up to help and literally had to lift Ron to standing. What used to be a simple outing had become quite complicated. I sensed our lives narrowing even more as the activities in which he could participate were becoming more limited.

The disease was clearly affecting his physical ability to move, be steady on his feet, and participate in life. Yet, when we engaged in an activity where we used the tiles from the Bananagram game to make words, Ron's "higher cognitive function" continued to show up in clever ways. It didn't seem like anything was wrong when he thought of "malevolent" and "mitigate" while looking for words that started with "m." And the night when I asked if he could think of a word in which we could use a "t," he responded with "sartorial." I had never heard that word before, so I went to the dictionary where I learned it refers to "tailoring, clothes, or style of dress."

Then there was the evening that Aleah and Jim came for dinner. Ron looked up and said, "Jim, how do you like the salad?"

And I had to laugh the day we were in the bathroom, and I was drying him off after his shower. He looked out the window and said something about the "vehicle" that was next door in our neighbor's driveway. It wasn't just a "car."

He still seemed to know who I was and could recognize the people in his family photos. He read signs and license plates non-stop when we were out in the car, and said, "I like taking rides so I can see what's going on around town."

He was also apparently keeping an eye on my driving.

One day, while taking him to daycare, I made a left turn at a busy intersection, and he told me I forgot to signal. When I asked him why he said that, he said, "Because you didn't roll down your window." Though he was clearly paying attention, he was obviously living in the era before turn indicators when you had to put your arm out the window to signal. Yet this was the guy who could no longer shower himself, was beginning to have trouble walking, was incontinent, and could barely feed himself.

As I saw more and more of the things we did together slip away due to Ron's increasing physical limitations and inconsistent behavior, I did my best to feel the losses when they occurred. I felt that strongly one morning when I went to the farmer's market, after leaving Ron at home with Caleb.

Over the years, we often enjoyed going there together early in the morning, then Ron would go home with the items we purchased after dropping me off at work. However, that morning, as I left the market, I was teary-eyed remembering the good times we'd had when things were "normal." Grieving the loss of those experiences seemed to be occurring more frequently.

When my sister, Nancy, invited us over for my birthday dinner that year, I became aware of yet another loss. Due to the difficulty in navigating stairs like those that led to her front door and the trouble I had getting Ron seated at a table, I suggested that she bring the food to our house, and everyone could come here. That way I could avoid the challenges involved in taking Ron out and managing him at her house.

When they arrived, Ron seemed glad to see them. It was my special day, but I adjusted it due to his needs. The traditions, even the times when we ate regular meals together or went over to someone's house for dinner, were gone. Yet, from another perspective, I was glad for the support of my family as they too adapted to the changes that were occurring with Ron.

One morning when Caleb was helping him get up, Ron again made a comment indicating that he was aware of the changing circumstances. He said, "I am in jail because I can't do what I want."

Evidently, that was how he experienced what I, too, was noticing, as both of our lives were more limited and becoming filled with experiences and tasks that we had not planned on.

Even though there was loss, and I could no longer live exactly as I wanted, it seemed a little easier when I could be aware of my feelings. After all, hadn't we set out to change our lives when we got married? When I could step back a bit further and observe all that I was learning and experiencing, I was even able to be grateful at times.

That was especially apparent a few weeks later when again, Ron and I were making words with the tiles from the Bananagram game. When

I asked him if he could think of a word that began with the letter "b," he said, "Beautiful." We went on to make more words, then, when we finished and I was cleaning up, I asked him what his favorite word from that game was.

He said, "Beautiful." When I asked him why, he said, "Because it reminds me of you." What a tender and touching moment!

As the disease progressed, I noticed that I was becoming less tolerant of the issues that occurred in other aspects of my life. Evidently, my "stress threshold" was bumped up. It felt like everything I had was going into caring for Ron, and I had little patience when other things didn't work out.

In the past, minor inconveniences had been issues that I successfully managed as a part of life. But the ease with which I was becoming upset by them was a good wake up call. I realized that I was stressed and needed to start being more consistent about taking care of myself. This journey was beginning to take a toll on me.

About that time, I came across an article by Rick Hanson from his book, *Just One Thing*, about watering your own fruit trees.[1] In the article, he spoke about the importance of nurturing yourself so you can bear the fruits of your being. He said that what you do doesn't have to be much and can be as simple as going to bed a bit earlier. However, he focused on the importance of seeing it as feeding yourself and not as something else to do.

I could relate. After all, I had literally been feeding Ron. What about me?

I must say I wasn't as consistent about doing that as I had hoped, as it was hard to find the time to add another thing to my life—even going to bed earlier.

The book, *The 36-Hour Day*, was becoming a reality. Lots to do and not enough time! However, as I found myself becoming more mindful of the difficult situations when they arose, I could deal with them in other ways. Then I wasn't as affected by the stress.

For instance, when I was getting Ron dressed to go to daycare, after putting his shirt on, I'd have him sit on the side of the bed and first, I would put his socks on, then his slacks. As long as he was sitting down, I'd squat down so I could put on his shoes and tie them. Then I would help him stand up and tuck in his shirt, pull up his slacks and zip them, finally putting on his belt. However, occasionally, while I was putting on his shoes, he would button his pants and zip them. Then in order to finish getting him dressed, I would first have to unbutton and unzip them.

One day I noticed myself getting really irritated by that, so instead of staying there feeling angry and getting impatient with Ron, I gave him his belt so he would have something with which to occupy himself, then I walked out of the room and paused, taking several deep breaths to help me calm down. When I returned, I was able to be kind and patient again.

However, the additional stress wasn't always so easy to manage. For several months, Ron would cough every night after we put him to bed, sometimes until well after midnight. Not only did that interfere with my sleep, but he would frequently experience incontinence of stool when he coughed which then had to be cleaned up. I was becoming exhausted.

Of course, with his Alzheimer's, Ron wasn't able to offer any feedback about what he felt might be causing the cough, so it was up to me, and the others who were with him, as well as the doctor, to try and figure it out.

After trying Benadryl then Zyrtec to resolve the cough with no results, the doctor looked further and discovered that one of the side effects of Lisinopril, the medication Ron was taking for high blood pressure, was dry cough. I immediately stopped giving that to him and the doctor wrote a prescription for something different for his blood pressure. In a little over a week, the coughing had subsided. *Voila!* That had been a long, hard period, and thankfully, it appeared to be coming to an end. The fix was so simple and yet it took a while to figure it out.

During the time that we were attempting to get to the source of Ron's coughing and inability to go to sleep, I was also trying to find ways to help him stay calm before going to bed. Since watching TV seemed to be stimulating, I directed him to his drawing which was comforting to him, and gave him a cup of chamomile tea. I then noticed other things that appeared to have a calming effect.

For instance, after eating something soft out of a bowl, he would use the spoon to circle the inside of the bowl, relentlessly. When he did it the day we had a friend over for soup I could see myself almost making a parental comment about not playing with your food. Though I would not have considered that good table manners in the past, I needed to let it go.

In fact, that gave me an idea. One day I experimented with putting a drop of honey on the plate from which I had been feeding Ron and let him spread that around with his finger for a while. I realized how comforting the circling activity was for him. Though I noticed my tendency to want to give him something more meaningful to do, I was finally learning to just let him be. Later, I even noticed that he was also rubbing circles on his hip, thigh, or knee when he was lying in bed or sitting in a chair. He was clearly using that motion to calm himself.

As Ron's general condition continued to decline, his walking became more and more impaired. I always took the wheelchair when we went out in the neighborhood as he could no longer go very far on his own. Thankfully, there was only one step to get out the front door, and one more from the porch to the sidewalk. With my help and by holding onto the handrail that Tom installed, he could still manage that.

That year on Valentine's Day, one of the daycare centers where I had been taking Ron had a party with a live band which provided music for dancing. Family members were invited to attend so I joined Ron. I don't recall the song we chose to dance to, but Ron's feet would barely move. We just swayed for a while. Eventually, I had to help him sit down so he wouldn't fall before the song was over.

I was devastated. I would no longer be able to dance with my husband. A wave of deep sadness washed over me.

Clearly, he could no longer walk or stand unassisted. I checked the website for the Alzheimer's Association and saw that one of the symptoms of the Late Stage was noted to be, "Needs assistance walking and eventually is unable to walk."[2] That would explain what I was seeing. And though many symptoms associated with the Late Stage had been present with Ron for some time, recently he was also having more difficulty in communicating.

One morning, when I was helping him get up, I said, "How do you feel today?" He replied saying, "How do you feel today?" But he wasn't asking me how I felt. He was just repeating what I said. That was happening more regularly. As the days went on, I found that when I gave

Ron a choice between two activities or two snacks, he could no longer make a decision. It was up to me to decide.

The frequency in his changes not only required that I pay more attention to what may be needed and get even more involved in his care, but I had to change our routines more often. It reminded me of nursing Aleah.

When she was a baby, I attended a breastfeeding support group where I learned about "frequency days." Those were defined as times when the baby was having a "growth spurt" and needed to increase the mother's supply of milk, which was done by nursing more frequently. Unfortunately, the frequency days I was experiencing while caring for Ron involved an increase in my involvement in his care which was related to a diminishment in his abilities as the disease continued to cause impairment. Just the opposite of a growth spurt.

Amid all this, Caleb said he was moving so he could help his mom out for a while. On the day his brother, Dan, came to help him move, the three of us talked about the future care and management of Ron. We all could see the increased changes that were occurring. It was good to be able to openly discuss it with his family. Having lived with us for almost nine months, Caleb understood very well what was involved in caring for his grandpa.

As a result of feeling the support I experienced from that conversation, I noticed that the next day I was able to care for Ron without feeling quite as stressed. It was interesting to see how helpful it was to be able to speak openly about his condition and his future needs with members of his family.

Though he no longer lived with us, Caleb continued to be available to care for Ron when I needed him. Ron's earlier caregiver, Steve, was also available to help take up the slack.

I was reminded that change is a natural part of life. As much as I wanted to hold onto the consistency of having Caleb live with us, I was glad I had gotten Ron on the waiting list at Namaste. When the day came for him to move there, that would be a big change.

Despite the changes in his abilities and his increasing needs for care, Ron still made comments that made me giggle. One day when I was shaving him, I said, "You're a good-looking guy," and he replied,

"The other teachers also tell me that." And another time when I was showering him, he told me the sheriff was coming to arrest me, though he couldn't tell me what I had done to deserve that.

One morning I was deeply touched by an interaction I had with him. When I got up to go to the bathroom around 4:30 a.m., I decided that as long as I was up, I would help Ron to the bathroom to change his Depends and get him a dry shirt. While he was sitting on the toilet, he started to whistle up a storm.

It made me laugh, especially given the time of day. As I carefully walked him back to bed I said, "It sounds like you're happy." Then I asked him why. He said, "It's because you're helping me." How could I not be happy too? In spite of everything, I was periodically getting glimpses that what I was doing mattered to him. That meant a lot.

It seemed to me that when Ron felt happy and loved, those emotions bypassed his confused brain and came from his heart. Interestingly, words were not needed to express it. Just whistling. Though he was far different from the man I had known before, it seemed like I was learning to love him in a new and deeper way.

Chapter 14

OVER THE COMING MONTHS, AS the decline in Ron's mobility and balance became more and more apparent, using the wheelchair was becoming a regular part of caring for him. However, in the research I had been doing about the Late Stage of Alzheimer's, I read about the importance of exercising the legs when the patient becomes more immobile. Thus, on the days when he seemed to have a little more energy, I acted as his walker, and we walked around the circle in the house several times to keep his legs working as long as possible.

I walked backwards facing him and put his hands on my shoulders. The added benefit of that was stopping to share an occasional hug. I hadn't realized how important it had been to me to be able to hold him next to me, not only when dancing but when I was helping him walk. It appeared that the day would come when I would no longer be able to get physically close to Ron, since there wasn't much room in the medical bed. I was becoming aware of the loss, but what about him? Since he had previously spoken about life now being different, he evidently was aware, though unable to name specific things.

Due to his decline, I began thinking about taking him to daycare just one afternoon a week, instead of several times. In considering whether I should do that, I talked with my friend Ginny, whose husband also had Alzheimer's. She said, "I understand perfectly what you are saying. Is he getting enough out of it to warrant the time and energy involved in getting him there, plus the expense? Does it give you any relief or is it just another stressor?"

There it was again—the need to consider how I was being affected by the decisions I was making. The extent to which I needed to factor that in was becoming more and more apparent.

Though I had been hearing about the importance of self-care ever since I went to the first class at the Alzheimer's Association, it felt like it didn't really begin to sink in until this stage when Ron's disease was requiring a lot more of me. But paying attention to my own wellbeing did not come easily. Putting others first and sometimes making choices that did not benefit me had been a lifelong pattern.

Apparently, seeing that the day would come when I would no longer have Ron in my life, was a wakeup call. Before too long, I would have to rely upon myself for my remaining years. The quality of my health and physical condition, as well as my emotional temperament, would be important in my ability to be comfortable and enjoy the time I had left.

Ron's unsteadiness, lack of mobility, and other physical changes continued to have a profound effect on our lives. Though I had gotten a car that had higher ground clearance and was easier to get into, he began having trouble just getting in the front passenger seat. I found myself coaching him and pushing and shoving him, yet he still ended up all slouched over and it was hard to put the seatbelt around him. Then, when I took him to daycare, I had to go through the whole exercise again in a few hours to bring him home.

One day after getting Ron ready for day care, we went to the garage. After trying unsuccessfully to help him get in the car, I found myself just standing there feeling almost numb and thinking to myself, "Is it worth it?" I felt stunned and didn't move for a while. After being with the reality of what was happening and thinking about my conversation with Ginny a few weeks before, I took him back in the house. I had an appointment for him with the dermatologist the next day and I canceled that, as well.

That was big. It was another reminder that this was the beginning of the end.

Even though I had been on this journey with Ron for over six years, at times I still had trouble changing the routines that I had developed along the way. Though I cancelled the immediate events after I couldn't get him in the car that day, I continued trying to figure out how I could take him out a few more times. I had to keep reminding myself that I was the one who had to change—again.

I knew I had to adjust my thinking about things and look for ways that I could adapt to his increasing needs. I wanted to see if I could take him out a few more times to do what seemed necessary and/or meaningful, even with the challenges of getting him in and out of the car.

I had been taking him to the lab at the doctor's office monthly to get his INR checked, since he was still on the Coumadin to prevent blood clots. Thankfully, I was able to get him in the car for the next test, but I wondered how I would even be able to accommodate that need in the months to come.

Then there was the dentist. We already had an appointment scheduled to have his teeth cleaned so I asked Caleb if he would go along and help me. Between the two of us we got Ron in the car then Caleb stayed with him during the appointment, helping to calm him, while I ran an errand nearby. Thankfully, Dr. Graton and his staff were patient and understanding with Ron.

And what about Ron's hair? It needed to be cut and it somehow felt like it would bring closure to have him see Cindy, who had been cutting his hair for years. I made an appointment and Steve went along to help with getting Ron into the car. As I think back on that, the "closure" was probably for me more than for Ron or Cindy.

Then there were two trips that I felt would be meaningful to Ron. One was paying a visit to his friends Bob and Jean, who had been a part of his life long before our marriage. When I called them, I learned that Bob's birthday was going to be in the next few days and due to his medical needs, they now had a wheelchair ramp leading to their front door.

That would make it easier to take Ron for a visit. On the day of Bob's birthday celebration, Caleb helped me get Ron and the wheelchair into the car at home. Luckily, when we got there, I was able to manage getting him out of the car and into the wheelchair. But knowing that I would have trouble getting him back in the car, Caleb offered to come help, so I called him when we were about ready to leave after having cake and ice cream with Bob and Jean.

Another outing that seemed like it would be meaningful to Ron was to visit my cousins who lived on a ranch less than an hour from town. He always loved going to see them. Not only were they friendly and understanding, but I think there was some link to the days that Ron spent visiting his cousins on a farm in Kansas when he was growing up.

Since it was summertime and the days were longer, I made arrangements for us to visit them over an evening meal, and again, Caleb helped me get Ron into the car when we left home. My cousin Jeff then helped me get him back in the car when we were ready to return.

On our way home, we got to witness a beautiful sunset to top off a wonderful evening. I enjoyed that and imagined Ron liking it as well. But he was no longer able to say much—not even whistle.

Throughout this period, I noticed that due to Ron's additional physical needs, I was experiencing some issues myself since I had to be more involved in helping him. I had discomfort in my hip and knee that I attributed to the way I had been pushing his chair into the kitchen table for his meals. I started getting massages and seeing my chiropractor regularly.

Since I was using a wheelchair with Ron by this time, I assumed I was no longer re-injuring myself. In an email "conversation" I was having with his kids I wrote, "I definitely want to make sure that I don't put myself in physical danger or stress overload as your dad's disease progresses."

When I heard myself being short with Ron and criticizing him while I was getting him ready for bed one evening, I recognized that was a sign that I was stressed. I paused to be aware and could see that I was not only tired after all I had done that day, but the decisions that needed to be made about Ron's care and current needs were also adding stress.

So, as a way to take care of myself, I made a schedule for either Caleb or Steve to come over after I fed Ron his dinner. They stayed with him and got him ready for bed, so I had the evenings to myself to do chores, take a walk, call a friend, whatever. It was my time. That made a big difference. Even the physical aspect of putting Ron into the bed had become difficult for me as he was like dead weight. After getting him in bed, Steve or Caleb would let me know, so I could kiss Ron and tell him goodnight.

In the midst of this period of Ron's decline, I received an email from Namaste where he was on the waiting list, indicating that they had a bed available, and I had a week to decide if I wanted it. Many of the things we had been going through pointed to the logic of moving him into their facility. In fact, I had thought about calling them on several occasions to let them know I was ready to place him. On one hand, I felt a sense of relief. Then the reality began to set in.

Initially I thought I would take the bed at Namaste for Ron, but then I realized that I would miss the moments I shared with him each day. I wondered if they would care for him as well as we were able to do at home. And of course, the cost of care was a concern. I had already spent quite a lot of Ron's money hiring folks to help me care for him both before and after I retired, including the day care and respite care. I didn't know how long I could pay for his care at Namaste, though I knew their charges were in line with many of the facilities that provided memory care, and that since he was losing his ability to function on his own, their classification as a skilled nursing facility was extremely important.

I emailed Curt, Tom, and Sara so I could get their input and together we processed the options for their dad. Curt and Sara still lived out of state at the time. Curt wrote that it seemed "too early" to place him, but he hadn't been around recently to see what was happening.

Tom came over the weekend and together we visited Namaste. He later shared in an email with the others, that he had a good impression of the place from the cleanliness and the number of staff caring for the patients, to the beautiful natural setting. In addition, having walked in unannounced, he was impressed that the chaplain graciously took her time to give us a tour. That was my impression as well.

He went on to write, "This decision is tough, mainly since we don't have the benefit of sure and certain predictions about Dad's abilities in the coming months. So we're left with the probabilities generated from patterns that we see, gut feelings, information about the nature of this disease, and counsel from others in the field or who have already moved through this phase with a loved one. Cyndy's opinion, her wisdom, and her experience with Dad in particular, carries the most weight in my mind." He further wrote that he saw me "struggling mightily with the decision," and that he could see how many conflicting emotions and thoughts came into play.

That was true. One day it felt like having Ron go to Namaste was best, then the next day it seemed just the opposite. I felt like a pendulum. Due to feeling this uncertainty, I was telling Tabitha, the social worker at Namaste, "Yes, I'll take the bed." Then the next day, I'd tell her, "I'm going to pass on the bed." I started to feel an increase in my anxiety. Why I thought I needed to update her every day, I don't know. Then I noticed I was imagining that Tabitha was thinking, "Who is this crazy woman who can't make up her mind?" And I was thinking, "So much for me feeling competent or even looking competent to others." I was definitely adding self-judgment to the situation, which only increased my stress.

I don't recall ever feeling so conflicted. In the midst of my uncertainty about placing Ron, I was talking to Steve. I told him it had been an easier decision for me to buy another house than this choice about placing Ron at Namaste, and he reminded me, "the house is just a thing." Ron was not only a human being, but he was my husband, a father, a grandfather, a brother, a friend.

There were many factors that went into the decision—many conflicting thoughts and emotions, as Tom pointed out. Initially, I had defined myself as Ron's wife, then I became his care partner. Who would I be if I no longer cared for him at home? And who would he be if he no longer lived with me? Just another one of "those patients?" Yet, the events of Ron's decline were starting to indicate that my ability to care for him was coming to an end. As much as I wanted to hold it together and be able to handle this, it felt like an avalanche as the pieces of our lives suddenly started falling apart even more and piling up on top of one another. But I loved him and letting go was scary. I was also becoming aware that on some level, it apparently meant to me that I would be a failure.

Finally, at the end of the week in which I had to decide, I told Namaste I was going to keep Ron at home for a while longer. On one hand I was willing to continue making adjustments so I could still meet his needs. Yet, at the same time, I had a lingering sense of uneasiness. I didn't know when another bed would be available, nor what was going to happen as he continued to decline. What if I wouldn't be able to manage him until then?

Chapter 15

WITHIN A COUPLE OF DAYS of making the decision to keep Ron at home and after settling back into a routine, Caleb and I noticed a change in his demeanor. In addition, we could tell that he had a fever as he was warm to the touch. Though I had not yet gotten a temporal thermometer, we knew better than to use the oral one after watching him bite it the last time we tried to take his temperature. Again, we suspected a UTI.

We wanted to get a urine sample so we could take it to the doctor's office for testing. We put the bucket on the toilet raiser and using it as a bedside commode, we put the urine collection container that we had gotten at the doctor's office inside. We had Ron sit on it but after about twenty minutes there was no pee. We thought that maybe if we put his feet in a basin of warm water, that would stimulate him to urinate. That didn't work either, but in the meantime, we noticed that the skin was sloughing off the bottom of his left heel, leaving a patch of raw skin. Now what? I could feel my anxiety rising.

We called the doctor's office and described our situation to one of the nurses. Within a few minutes I received a call from the doctor and after listening to the story, he said he would call in a prescription of Cipro which had been used to treat Ron's UTI previously. Thankfully, he was willing to do that.

As the days went on, Ron didn't seem to respond to the Cipro as he had in the past and we noticed an additional loss of strength and coordination in his legs. In addition, we then had the heel wound to address. I called a nurse I knew who worked at the hospital in wound care, and she gave us some suggestions. It was beginning to feel like I was in over my head.

This experience was timely in that it helped me see the importance of focusing on how we were going to meet Ron's medical needs at home. I realized that in no longer being able to take him out, I would need to get some sort of help for non-emergent medical issues that arose. I would also need help with routine issues such as his monthly blood tests. I recalled hearing that our local hospice had a program for palliative care as opposed to complete hospice care, so I made an appointment for a nurse to come do an evaluation.

On the day of her visit, after hearing what I told her about Ron's journey and his current condition, the hospice nurse said she felt he might qualify for the regular hospice program. She made a call to consult with a physician on their staff, and Ron was accepted. That came as a surprise to me. I had been a hospice volunteer and thought that would have meant he was nearing the end. I couldn't seem to really grasp that they were willing to admit him to their regular hospice program.

Although Alzheimer's was a terminal disease and Ron was in the late stage, I didn't feel like he was going to die in the coming months. At the same time, I was grateful, as having the involvement of the hospice staff meant that I would have the input of medical professionals in making decisions beyond the day-to-day care being provided by me and others. I felt like a huge burden had been lifted.

During Ron's intake process which involved a consulting with the hospice physician, we decided to take him off the Coumadin and the medication he was taking for his high blood pressure. That solved my concern about not being able to take him in for his monthly INR so his Coumadin dose could be adjusted.

It felt right. Why continue to do things that were prolonging his life? That was similar to the decisions I made earlier, when I took him off the CPAP machine and chose not to have him get a colonoscopy.

We had turned a corner from trying to support Ron in maintaining his health, to acknowledging where he was in the process of the disease. It wasn't that we were giving up. It was just that the focus was shifting to "end of life care."

We also agreed not to call 911 should there be an emergency, but to contact hospice. They provided a "comfort kit" that I could use, should an event occur where Ron was in distress before the hospice nurse could arrive. It included such things as a pain reliever and medications for anxiety, as well as nausea and vomiting. I marked it clearly and put it in the refrigerator.

Hospice also provided some bandages and care instructions for Ron's heel wound. We determined that was evidently caused by his heels having increased contact with the bed as he became less active because his other heel was beginning to show similar problems. In the classes I took, I had learned about the importance of making sure to help our loved ones shift positions while in bed, to avoid pressure sores. I had been keeping a close eye on Ron's bony points in the area of his shoulders and hips, as I often saw that his skin was sometimes red in those areas when he woke up in the mornings. I even used extra pillows to prop him on one side or the other to minimize that. But I never thought about looking at his heels.

I also didn't directly encounter that part of his body when I was showering or dressing him. Looking back, it probably would have been helpful to have gotten one of the alternating-pressure, inflatable medical mattress pads when he started spending so much time in bed in order to alleviate pressure sores. I later saw an excellent description of skin breakdown, also known as "decubitus ulcers" on the website, *The Dementia Queen*.[1]

We also started to pay more attention to another physical issue we had been noticing for a while. Ron was developing contractures, which I had learned were common during the Late Stage of Alzheimer's. It was initially noticeable in his left hand when the last three fingers were clenched for long periods of time, with his fingertips pressed against the palm of his hand. The *Dementia Queen*, describes contractures as, "a chronic loss of joint motion caused by shortening of a muscle or tendon." It stated further that, "in Late-Stage Alzheimer's disease, contractures of the knees, elbows, and hands form mostly from lack of movement enhanced by neurologic changes in muscle tone, making joints more resistant to passive movement."[2]

We then noticed some movement limitations in his left leg as he became less mobile. With everything else going on, those seemed like the least of our worries, but when we had time, one of us would massage Ron's fingers or thigh, and gently extending them.

By this time, my son-in-law Jim was helping when he could, as was Ron's grandson, Dan. We had a well-trained team.

It was very touching to see the love and tenderness that the guys exhibited in caring for Ron. With the help of Hospice and the others in overseeing his needs, I could feel myself being weaned and distanced from my intense and intimate involvement with him.

I felt sad. That seemed like a huge loss. Yet, I realized it was important to let myself feel it. Those were no doubt the same feelings I had unconsciously felt around making the decision about whether or not to place him at Namaste, and they would no doubt be there again if I didn't become fully aware of them. It was all part of the shifts and adjustments that were occurring as we entered into this new phase.

As his family and I assessed what would be needed in the weeks to come with Ron still living at home, two things stood out. An obvious one was that, since he was losing the ability to walk and we were primarily using the wheelchair to get him around, we were no longer able to take him outside. It was summertime, and even though we were not taking him out in the car, certainly he would still enjoy going to the park up the street and spending time on the patio.

Curt said he would like to come spend some time with his dad and he could build a ramp to accommodate the two steps that were involved when taking Ron out the front door. Tom said he would come to help with that, too.

I also saw that it would be helpful for me to have some respite and get away for a few days. Since they were going to be here, I could take time for myself. Curt and Tom said that would be okay, so I contacted Karen to see if I could spend a few days with her and Lyle. She said yes. Things seemed to be falling into place.

It had been quite a while since Curt had seen his dad and he was here for several days before I left. After he arrived, I heard him say repeatedly, "We need to do everything we can to get Dad walking again."

I tried to explain that Ron was experiencing a symptom of the Late Stage and that his brain cells were no longer capable of firing the nerves that worked his legs. I also told him about the exercises that I had done with Ron up until recently and how I had tried to encourage him to walk. Then, I explained how folks with Alzheimer's can push themselves to "act normal" in the presence of others and that his dad might be doing that to try to please him. But Curt didn't seem to understand what I was saying. His focus was on getting his dad to walk, like this was just a temporary set-back and some rehab would do the trick.

I then left for my get-away, leaving the team, plus Curt and Tom, to look after Ron while they were building the ramp.

I returned a few days later to find a beautiful wooden ramp in front of the house. I paid Curt for the expenses involved in building it. Tom had already gone home; then Curt went to spend a few days with his mom before leaving town.

The next day, Dan came over to help with Ron's morning routine. Sara had gotten into town the day before, so she came with him. She, too, wanted to see her dad due to his recent decline.

The sunshine was streaming in the bedroom on the wooden floor when Dan got Ron up to take him to the bathroom. In spite of the three of us coaching Ron to move his legs, he could not seem to do it. While Dan and Sara held him, I put the bucket on the commode and moved it to the middle of the room so they could help Ron sit down on it. His obvious inability to move felt like it was amplified by the fact that the three of us witnessed it simultaneously.

Although I knew that difficulty in moving was a normal part of the Late Stage, seeing Ron unable to take a step that morning was, for me, one of the most intense moments of our journey.

After we finished cleaning Ron up and getting him dressed, Dan and Sara took him to the park in the wheelchair using the new ramp. While they were gone, I made breakfast with tears in my eyes.

When they got home, we wheeled Ron up to the dining room table then joined him to eat the pancakes I had made. He was too tired to eat, even if we fed him, so we took him back to bed.

Dan, Sara, and I ate, interestingly avoiding any discussion of what we had just witnessed and the experience earlier in the bedroom. Sara talked primarily, telling us about what she had been going through in the last few months since her husband left her without any preliminary indication that their marriage was not working. Clearly that was a very stressful time in her life, and I could see how it would be hard to see the other primary male in her life, her dad, leaving, as well.

When we finished eating, they left.

The hospice nurse was scheduled to come that day, early in the afternoon. When Ron woke up from his nap, Steve got him ready for lunch, and I made him a sandwich. While we were doing that Curt called to see how his dad was doing. I tried to explain about the events of the morning when Ron had been unable to take even one step, and then said I needed to go so I would be ready to meet with the nurse who was coming shortly.

When the nurse arrived, we talked about the challenges regarding Ron's care, then he examined Ron. I expressed my concern about Ron no longer being able to walk and talked about how hard it had been to that morning when Dan and Sara were here.

A little later, just as the nurse was preparing to leave, Curt pulled up. He came in and proceeded to tell the nurse he thought it was important to exercise his dad so he could walk again. I could feel my frustration build.

I had explained the reasons for Ron's increasing difficulty with walking when Curt first came to town; and I had relayed the events that occurred that morning when he called. I had been doing my best to help Ron keep walking as long as he could. I felt disrespected. Curt had not expressed interest in coming to that meeting when we talked on the phone earlier, then he suddenly showed up. It felt like he thought he was right, and I didn't know what I was talking about.

I blurted out something like, "I bust my butt caring for your dad and I think I know what I'm doing." I felt so angry that I needed to leave the room. It was only the second time in my life I had felt that angry.

From the mindfulness perspective I had clearly gotten hooked into an old pattern. Curt's comment triggered a place in me where I felt like I could never be good enough to please others. The stress I was feeling from the entire situation showed up in my comment to him.

Had I been more present in that moment, I could have noticed the feelings of inadequacy arising, taken a deep breath and reassured myself that I was taking good care of Ron, doing what was best for him in the continually changing situations that arose. I then could have proceeded to respond to Curt without the anger.

At least I paused and didn't remain in the room, where I might have added some unhelpful comments. Finally, after calming down I went back and Curt and I were able to make amends, with a little bit of coaching from the hospice nurse. During that time Curt said something about our phone call earlier and the nurse asked him what I said. Curt told him I said we weren't going to do anything more for his dad. Then Steve spoke up. Having overheard the telephone conversation, he said, "She did not say any such thing."

Curt and I finished making amends via email the next day. I was able to tell him that when he made those comments, I felt he did not respect all I learned and had been doing to care for his dad; nor was he respecting his dad in expecting him to walk when he was clearly unable to do so. By the time we finished our conversations and emails, I felt like Curt understood and was appreciative of what I was doing.

Looking back, I understood Curt's concern about his dad. Having been involved in several similar situations when I worked at the hospital, I was aware that when family members are not present to the day-to-day events of caring for a loved one, the desire to get things under control and back to normal can be an overriding factor instead of accepting what is actually occurring. I had been that way myself early on in Ron's disease.

It played out a little differently for Sara after seeing her dad that morning in his current condition, with everything she also had going on in her own life. In an email the next day, she explained that taking her dad to the park that morning had been a special time for her to love him and she wasn't "filled with sadness" during that time. She wrote that she had been involved in caring for her mother-in-law during her terminal phase and death, and she didn't want to relive those memories with her dad, especially since she didn't live here. Thus, though she was in town for a week, those few hours she spent with Ron that morning was the only time Sara saw him.

Emotionally, it was hard for all of us. Each of us were at different points in the journey with Ron, and in our lives. It was important to acknowledge that, and despite not feeling the same support from Curt and Sara that I felt from those who were more involved in Ron's day-to-day care, I tried to understand.

I couldn't let myself be pulled off into trying to fix the experiences they were having or convince them about the care that I was giving their dad. Nor could I let myself feel abandoned by them. I did my best to understand what they were going through, while at the same time, stay focused on the needs of Ron and myself.

Chapter 16

GOING FORWARD, I NEEDED HELP caring for Ron almost eight hours every day. At times, that was difficult as the guys had their own lives and could not commit to a regular schedule. I often scrambled to get enough help. Nights were hard, but I didn't feel comfortable with someone else being at the house while I was asleep, especially someone from an agency. Nor did I feel I could afford it.

The hospice nurse came weekly to check the wounds on Ron's heels. In spite of caring for them and re-bandaging them daily, as well as using antibiotic ointment on them, they did not seem to be improving, and in fact, one got a nasty odor as a result of necrosis of the tissue.

Due to my difficulty managing Ron's increasing immobility, it was even getting hard for me to help him to the bedside commode. The hospice sent a CNA out to demonstrate how to do a bed bath and change a diaper without getting him out of bed. We were coming to the end of using the pull-on Depends, the toilet, and even the bedside commode. In fact, I already had an experience where I cut the sides of a pair of

Depends in order to take them off, instead of pulling them down over Ron's legs.

That instruction session with the CNA was just in time. The next morning Jim, Aleah's husband, was scheduled to help me with Ron but he had injured his shoulder doing karate, so she came along. We donned the gloves and began to clean Ron up, only to discover that his diaper was very full of poop, so we had a chance to put into practice what I had learned the day before. It was hard but we managed. Afterward, Aleah, again reminded me to care for myself, and suggested that maybe it was time for Ron to go to Namaste.

Later that day I wrote in my journal. I noted that I was having trouble staying focused and was finding myself just wandering around aimlessly, feeling ungrounded. I made note of my uncertainty around the care and ultimate life of Ron. That "uncertainty" experience felt like it was more intense than the previous ones. It seemed like doing the right thing to ensure that he could get the best care, and at the same time taking care of myself, had jumped to a new level.

I saw that wanting to have a purpose and not seem like a failure, were influencing my hesitancy to place him. I also was afraid I would be lonely if I wasn't caring for Ron. I knew that if I could experience those thoughts and feelings with awareness, I would make better choices.

Interestingly, later that day, I read some articles on The Family Caregiver Alliance site. They described the effect on both physical and mental health that can come with being a caregiver. One of the articles spoke to how the caregivers' health often becomes worse as the patient's condition declines. The line that got my attention said, "The physical stress of caregiving can affect the health of the caregiver, especially when providing care for someone who cannot transfer him/herself out of bed, walk or bathe without assistance."[1]

That was exactly what Ron required. Clearly, I needed to make some changes.

The involvement of hospice included a meeting with their social worker. However, that meeting had been postponed due to Curt and Tom being here and me being out of town for a few days. So, after getting back into a more normal routine, the social worker and I scheduled a meeting.

When she heard about the stress I was experiencing due to the decline in Ron's condition, she suggested that I contact Tabitha at Namaste again to give her an update. When I emailed Tabitha, she responded, saying they just had a male bed become available in the Late-Stage unit. She suggested that I come to look at it.

I went over the next morning and signed Ron up on the spot. We made plans for him to move in the following day. That was far different than the uncertainty I experienced when the previous bed was available.

There was no hesitation this time; I was ready. Having gone through the process a few weeks earlier and seeing the changes that had occurred with Ron, as well as having become more aware of some of my own feelings about placing him, I was certain. I felt completely comfortable with my decision.

I don't even recall feeling rushed in having only one day to get him prepared. Later that day I got his clothes laundered and organized to take. I put Ron's name in them, as was suggested by Namaste, since they sometimes laundered the residents' clothing together in the same load.

Tabitha said the best time to bring Ron would be late in the afternoon. At that time, the staff would be more available to help us get him situated. She invited me to stay for a while and have dinner with him.

Since Ron could no longer get in the car, I made arrangements with a homecare company that provided a wheelchair transport van, to pick him up the next afternoon. I asked Caleb to ride in the van with Papa so he wouldn't be alone. I drove separately so we would have a car in which to return home.

All went well getting Ron into the van. I hadn't told him anything about the move, as that seemed like it would be an abstract concept to him. I thought it would be more meaningful to talk about staying at the new place when we got him settled in his room at Namaste. I put his clothes, his toothbrush and shaving kit, a few family pictures, plus his drawing pad and pencils in the car and pulled out of the driveway to follow the van. I had to focus on driving safely, through my tears.

After we arrived at Namaste and got Ron situated in his room, I put away his clothing and other items. I decided to save putting the pictures on his bulletin board for another day. We used a bright quilt that Sara had made for him as a cover for his bed. We introduced the staff to him, then the nurses came in to look at Ron's heel wounds.

Soon, dinner was served. They had prepared a table where just the three of us could sit together. Following dinner, we wheeled Ron around to show him the place, and then helped him get settled at a table with his drawing pad and pencils before we left. Thankfully, he didn't seem to show any anxiety or concern.

I wondered if having taken him to daycare and respite care over the years may have helped him with that transition.

During the drive home with Caleb, I felt both sad about no longer having Ron at home, and grateful to have finally made the decision and to have him live in such a beautiful place for the last period of his life—however long that was going to be.

In the days that followed, I noticed the "empty nest" at home. Not only was Ron gone, but all the guys, as well as the hospice staff, were no longer coming. It went from a very busy place to just me. With more time on my hands and the sudden changes, I found myself cleaning up the bedroom and bathroom. I would no longer need the trash can with the lid for Ron's dirty Depends and diapers. The bedside commode, transport chair and shower chair could go to the basement. For now, I would leave the hospital bed in place as I was not in a hurry to totally make the room mine. I then found myself cleaning the whole house. Staying busy helped!

I also sent emails about Ron's move to the extended family and friends. His brother, Max, wrote that he had been in touch with Sara and Curt and thanked me for consulting with Ron's children and grandchildren prior to making the decision to move him to Namaste.

Curt wrote that he agreed with Max's comments and thanked me for talking through his concerns previously. He concluded, saying, "I am really grateful that Tom, Sara, and I had the opportunity to see Dad last month and spend some time with him at home. That means a lot to all of us, and we really appreciate it."

The day after Ron's move, Sara wrote, "I am thinking of you and know it will be a day full of lots of emotions, sadness and relief, all mixed together. Thank you for all you have done for Dad and will continue to do as he transitions to a new setting."

Despite the stress we had all been going through, I was glad that we were able to pull together in support of Ron.

For a while after Ron went to Namaste, I went to see him six days a week, accompanied by other family members at times. The staff was wonderful in listening to my suggestions about caring for him, and after several weeks I could see him relaxing and adjusting to his new surroundings. Since he was in the hospice program, their staff was involved in his care at Namaste, as well.

I was extremely grateful for the natural setting in which Namaste was located. Not only did I know that Ron would be at home in that environment, but I also found it soothing for me. Since it was July, my visits generally included taking him outdoors where I wheeled him around the pond. At times, we had to stop to wait for deer to move from the path. Other times, I paused to sit on one of the benches with Ron's wheelchair beside me, so we could take in the sights, sounds, and smells of nature.

For me, those pauses were also a time when my sadness bubbled up. It felt important to allow the tears to be there. I was seeing that in letting Ron be cared for by others, I could start taking better care of myself.

Yet, at the same time, I still missed him at home. I would be making coffee in the morning and suddenly feel like I had forgotten to crush his meds, which had been a part of my morning routine. Then, at other times when I got busy, I'd suddenly stop and think I needed to go check on Ron.

About a month after he moved into Namaste, the hospice nurse told me that Ron had an open wound in the area of his tailbone, as well as the sores on his heels. One day while I was visiting, the nurses were changing him and included me so I could see what they were talking about. The wound was deep, and the nurses were careful to reposition him on his side when they finished so there would not be any pressure on his tailbone.

Seeing yet another decline in Ron's physical health seemed to take me to a deeper level of grief. When I left that day, I cried all the way home. He was so sweet, yet he was so gone. And he was now dealing with medical issues as well.

I noticed thinking maybe the sooner the better, for him to die. I was shocked at myself feeling that way. But how much more did he have to endure, and how much longer did I have to watch him suffer? Or maybe he wasn't suffering. Maybe it was harder for me than it was for him.

At that time, Ron was the only surviving husband of the friends I had met at the day care center. The others had already passed away.

One day, in a conversation I was having with Marjorie, she said, when recalling her journey with Carl, "We don't know what to wish for our spouses. We all struggle with wanting them to have a meaningful life and there's a point where that no longer seems reasonable. It's hard to know where to draw the line."

I had had similar conversations with other friends. We didn't want them to suffer, yet when was enough, enough? That was another reminder that there really were no rules, nor did we have any control over how the disease would progress. We just had to be with the experience as it unfolded each day.

I was doing my best to be with the new feelings and concerns I was facing after no longer being responsible for Ron's care. I noticed feeling an increase in my anxiety about the future, wondering if our finances would hold out for the duration of his stay at Namaste.

I also began to feel new levels of loneliness. When I walked in the neighborhood, I was flooded with memories of doing that with Ron, both when he could walk with ease and more recently when his walking was impaired or when he was in the wheelchair.

I was watching the life I had once envisioned sharing with him come to a slow and agonizing close. I even found myself having more memories of the activities we shared before Alzheimer's.

One Sunday afternoon, I was suddenly overcome with sadness, remembering the typical Sundays while I was working, when I would take the time to cook a nice dinner.

Dan and Aleah joined me for the Walk to End Alzheimer's that year, and as we walked, we shared memories of Ron. Dan remembered sharing activities in nature with him when he was younger, and Aleah recalled him coaching her when she won the fifty-yard dash in elementary school. I remembered the many times Ron and I had walked on that same trail along the creek, and the year when we went there daily to see the moose that had come to town.

After the Walk we went to Cy's for a hamburger, then to the drive-in where Ron and I had routinely taken the grandkids for soft ice cream cones. While we were visiting those places from the past, our memories about Ron shifted to current times during his journey with Alzheimer's.

Dan said one day he kissed him on the forehead and Ron asked why he did that. When Dan told him, he did it because he loved him, Ron replied, "Well you can keep doing it then."

I recalled a recent Sunday at Namaste when I went to visit Ron just as he was finishing his breakfast. I took him out to sit by the pond, but it was a cool day, so our time outside was brief. As we were going back in, I saw the stained-glass windows in the chapel at the end of the hall and wheeled him there so we could sit together a little longer. Wondering what we could talk about, since we were in the chapel, I asked him if there was anything for which he was thankful. He said, "I'm thankful for you." Though Ron's memory continued to fade, it seemed that there were still times when we could feel close.

Since I had been accustomed to cutting Ron's nails, trimming his beard, and cleaning out his nostrils when he could no longer blow his nose while he was living at home, those seemed like things I could continue to do at Namaste. Even though most of his care was being provided by the staff, I still wanted to be involved in caring for him aside from just visiting, though I decided to leave his pedicures to the podiatrist who came to Namaste and paid the minimal charge for that.

I got a cape at a local beauty supply shop and periodically, when the weather was nice, I would take Ron's beard trimmers, and do his grooming outside by the pond. However, the hairdresser said I could also use the beauty shop when she wasn't there. One day when I was trimming his hair in the beauty shop, I noticed a deep reverent feeling for him. Our time together in that moment felt sacred.

Even though I still was involved in his care, I could relax a bit and actually be with him when I visited Namaste. That was considerably different after so many years of doing it all. In talking to a friend, I described this period as being an "in between" time with a focus on both Ron and me. He and I were having opposite experiences. While he was slowly phasing out, it felt like a time for me to determine how I was going to move on and begin to step into the new life that I would be living. Overall, I also seemed to be feeling more confident.

As time went on, I when was feeling the loss of Ron and of what was familiar to me, I found myself becoming aware not only of the sadness, but also of the uncertainty I was feeling. In the process of using my mindfulness practice more regularly, I noticed that I was shifting from trying to figure things out and instead, learning to trust the process. It had taken a long time for me to incorporate this new way of doing things, but I was glad to be opening to other ways of being in life.

I was reminded of my journey as Ron's care partner when I read an article in *Mindful Magazine* entitled "The Scary, Winding Road through Change." It dealt with navigating the transitions that come with change. That road was familiar to me, as it seemed to be the one I was taking with Ron.

Though I did my best to learn about the route, there was no map. I had to make choices about which way to go and how to navigate whatever was right in front of me. Sometimes the road was smooth and sometimes it had potholes. Always the destination was uncertain, and as I was learning, "The old rules don't seem to apply anymore."[2]

An overriding aspect of learning to navigate by letting life show me the way, seemed to be having an intention versus setting a goal. One day, Karen and I exchanged an email conversation about living life based on our intentions and moving along moment by moment versus setting goals to get it to turn out a certain way.

I mentioned that in general, it seemed like setting a goal usually resulted in a more linear process, often with steps to follow and points to reach along the way. I wrote further that intentions are broader and more inclusive. For instance, when caring for Ron, knowing that with Alzheimer's each day and each situation is so different, there was no way I could guarantee meeting a goal. That was a big part of learning how to navigate without a map.

Instead, I found that when I had an intention to care for Ron to the best of my ability and have him be as comfortable as possible, while looking out for myself at the same time, I could let the process show me. That meant that I had to be aware of what was happening, let go of thinking about the "right way" to do it, and be open to another way of seeing it.

I also noted that in trusting the process, it was necessary to stay in the moment and be present to the journey versus striving for something in the future. In fact, it was only then that the next step became apparent. It was a result of me staying personally engaged and present, versus applying something from outside to direct me. And while the result remained unknown until the end, it reflected my intention.

In using that approach, I was also seeing that I could trust myself to handle whatever arose. That did not mean that I had to have it figured out or do it by myself. I had learned that it was okay not to know and to ask for help without feeling that I was a failure. I told Karen that process was helping me see the subtle and assumed cultural messages and expectations that had kept me "in my place" all these years. Wow. I was amazed that caring for Ron seemed to be resulting in the personal freedom that I had longed for and struggled to achieve for so long.

Having the time and space to feel my feelings and reflect on them while he was still a part of my life, was huge. I was very grateful for that opportunity and, to a larger extent, for the gifts that Ron having Alzheimer's, was bringing to my life.

Chapter 17

As THE YEAR CAME TO an end, one day when I went to see Ron the staff told me that he experienced a big episode of choking on his food the night before.

I wasn't surprised. I had seen it coming both with food as well as his saliva. I read that for those in the late stage, having their swallowing impaired was a symptom that many experienced, along with being impaired in their mobility.

The head of the dietary department met with me and explained that in such cases, the residents are given food that has been pureed so it's easier for them to swallow it. I noticed others in the area where Ron's room was located who were already on that diet. And in many cases, they also had to be fed by the staff. It was all part of the continuing decline due to the disease. Though it was hard to witness, based on the past, I knew I would adjust. I had been helping Ron with his eating since before he went to live at Namaste. I had even gotten a baby food grinder to have in case I needed to soften his food while he was still at home, but I was grateful that I didn't have to use it. Now, I could rely on Namaste to manage the transition to a different diet.

Though I was getting some reprieve in not having to care for Ron directly, the journey was taking on more challenges. I noticed that worry and uncertainty were cycling around for me once again, this time related primarily to the cost of his care at Namaste. Ron had already been living there for six months, and in not knowing how much longer he would be with us, I could see that was something I needed to address before our resources were depleted.

Simultaneously, the issue regarding how I was going to go on with my life after Ron died was becoming more relevant. On top of that were the feelings of sadness and loss due to the continual changes that were occurring with him. I was reminded again of how much I still wanted to hold onto "normal." Not the old normal but just the way it had been when I was caring for him at home.

I saw the degree to which I had grown accustomed to being Ron's wife. In grieving the loss of him, I was also grieving the loss of that part of myself and the safety I had experienced in those roles. Even being his care partner had become familiar.

Though the journey of moving beyond the rules and roles of our pasts was fundamental to the reason we came together in the first place, it was not easy. I could see that it would have been more difficult for me to release my past limitations had our relationship remained relatively normal.

In an email I sent to a friend, I wrote, "It feels like the culmination of a lifetime of stuff cycling through, going deeper, and releasing." I mentioned the value of being present to the process as well as the grieving and release of the emotions that accompanied it.

It helped to have a connection to others who were going through the same thing. I remember Helen who was caring for her husband, when she spoke of it as life "re-forming" itself. I liked that analogy.

Another friend said, "Things change, and we have to change with it." Indeed, our spouses were not the men we knew in the past. And neither were we the women we had been in the past. I was glad to be getting a glimpse of the new strengths and courage that had emerged in me, amidst the feelings of fear and loss.

I was grateful for my friendships with the spouses of other Alzheimer's patients, who I had met in my support groups. And with Ron being at Namaste, I was beginning to connect with others who's loved ones now lived there.

Frequently, especially on the days when it was too chilly to go outside, I wheeled him around after his meals so I could meet and chat with the family members who were also visiting their loved ones.

I discovered that the connections with others were fascinating. A woman who had been Ron's dental assistant visited Namaste periodically to see her aunt and occasionally looked in on Ron as well. Interestingly, I had worked at the hospital with her cousin, who was the one to place her mother at Namaste.

We knew Helen and her husband from graduate school. She and I reconnected after running into each other at a workshop sponsored by the Alzheimer's Association. She had placed Bill at Namaste when he became confined to a wheelchair following multiple falls when trying to walk.

The day I stopped to talk to Ray, whose wife, Mary, recently came to Namaste, I learned that he had worked at Hewlett Packard before retiring to care for Mary. I asked if he knew my neighbor, Dave, who had also worked there and whose wife now had Alzheimer's. Ray said he did and said he would like to see Dave again, especially now that they had both become Alzheimer's caregivers. I told him I would talk to Dave about arranging a time and place where we could all get together. But before I could do that, Mary passed away and Ray was no longer coming to Namaste.

I had also gotten involved with the family council that met monthly with one of the administrators of Namaste, in order to establish good communication and make sure we had a voice in the organization. There I met other family members and that helped me feel like I had expanded my role a little bit and had a new purpose. It was even similar to some of the meetings that were part of my job when I worked at the hospital.

In giving more consideration to the options for moving on in my life after Ron passed away, I realized I had already been sharing mindfulness with my caregiver friends by doing small classes while our loved ones were at daycare. Due to the value it seemed to provide to those of us in the caregiver role, I began to look more closely at ways I could expand my teaching to others with a similar focus.

About that time, I learned of a year-long program at UCLA that provided a certification in mindfulness facilitation, so I applied. In the past, I would have been hesitant to jump right into something with the financial, time, and travel requirements of that program, especially due to the uncertainty of my current situation. But not this time. I surprised myself! I applied, and I was accepted.

Along with weekly assignments and group conference calls, we were required to be on campus for several days, four times during the year. That stretched me further out of my comfort zone, and my life continued to "re-form," since I was finding ways to move on without Ron. Being in that program also gave me the opportunity to expand my group of friends beyond those who were other Alzheimer's caregivers. I was slowly discovering a new me.

While I was doing my coursework for the certification program, I began to address our financial situation in light of spending over $7,000 a month for Ron's care. I learned about Jennifer through one of my contacts in the community. She was a financial counselor who specialized in Medicaid, so I scheduled an appointment with her.

After my first session, I walked out of her office feeling extremely grateful for the fact that I learned about her, and she was so knowledgeable. I wouldn't have to figure it all out by myself. She explained how we could qualify for assistance from Medicaid for Ron's care. *(Appendix 2)*

She then gave me a list of the information I would need to gather for the application process, which included past tax returns, account balances, etc. She advised me how I could legitimately spend some of Ron's funds to fix up the house a bit. She explained that one of the benefits of Medicaid was that it was designed so that spouses in my situation would not become impoverished as a result of caring for their loved one and could live comfortably and take care of themselves after their spouse had passed.

The process of applying for and receiving Medicaid support for Ron's care was, at times, embarrassing. I noticed feeling ashamed of not having done a better job of managing my life financially. Yet, when I was able to bring awareness to those feelings and beliefs, I was kind to myself and let them go. In going through the process with Jennifer, I was allowing myself to be supported in a new way. I was already being supported by the Namaste staff who were caring for Ron. Now, to make my life going forward more comfortable, I could keep an allowed amount of money from our savings and investments and would not have to use any of my monthly retirement income to provide for his ongoing care. That was a huge relief.

I also felt additional support from Ron's family as Sara was moving back to town since she had gotten divorced, and the others were going to see Ron periodically.

Despite having a lot going on, I still managed to go see Ron several times a week. That summer was the one-year anniversary of his move to Namaste, and I noticed myself beginning to feel kind of burned out in taking time to see him regularly.

At the same time, it felt like I was deepening my ability to be with Ron in his decline. I continued to sing, "I Love You a Bushel and a Peck" to him. But now, when I paused for him to sing his part, he mumbled the words which were barely audible. He was drooling much of the time and had to be fed all the time, which gave me an opportunity to feel connected to him.

Though he was on pureed food, his difficulty in swallowing, even his saliva, continued. I tried to time my visits with mealtime, usually the noon meal. That was when they served dinner, with the evening meal being lighter, more like lunch. Thankfully, Ron was cooperative about being fed, compared to some of the other residents I observed.

Following both the breakfast and the noon meal, the staff helped Ron into his bed for a nap, as he was sleeping more and more. When I was there, I usually stayed while they changed him and got him into bed, after which they lowered his bed and put pads on the floor on either side, so he wouldn't get injured should he roll off the edge or try to get up. I was grateful that I was able to help. The staff was always very kind to him and to me.

Since my responsibilities in caring for him were minimal, it felt like, aside from feeding him and pushing him around in his wheelchair, there was nothing else to do but love Ron when I was with him. I frequently took time to sit with him after the staff got him into bed and left his room. I had taken the book of poems that he wrote as well as another book of poetry that he had in his bookcase at home so I could read poetry to him. I could tell he liked that. A calmness would come over him as he drifted off to sleep.

It seemed like I was tapping into a kind of love that I had not experienced before with Ron. When I tuned in, it felt like I was just *being love*—much different than being *in love*. It seemed to be a result of my continual adjusting during our years on the Alzheimer's journey, when I saw various parts of him slipping away. Though it took a while initially, I finally caught on.

Marguerite Manteau-Rao, in her book, *Caring for a Loved One with Dementia*, when referring to her experience while caring for her mother, said, "True love is purified from all attachment..."[1] That explained it. I was evidently learning to love Ron with no expectations or attachments.

As I became more able to understand what he was experiencing, I learned new ways to be with him that seemed to help him be at peace and enjoy what life he had. In discovering a new way to love, I discovered that I was caring more about myself as well.

I got a better understanding of my experience when I was reading, *Awakening Through the Nine Bodies*, by Phillip Moffitt. He wrote that, "All love is already within you... as pure love without attachment or expectation. It is there for your discovery."[2]

Earlier in the book, he described it as a love that is "not romantic or self-referenced, but rather (a) mysterious, interdependent oneness."[3] He later referred to it as "unconditional love."[4] That seemed to be a good way of explaining what I was tapping into.

In her book, *A Deeper Perspective on Alzheimer's and Other Dementias*, Megan Carnarius spoke of the way in which caregivers and family members must continually reorient themselves as the disease progresses. She spoke of the importance of being able to allow "what is, to be," so they do not "drive themselves into paralyzing grief."[5]

It had taken me a while to learn that, but by continually bringing myself back to the moment, I was able to be more present with what was occurring and allow it to be, without an expectation or concern about how it would turn out.

Rev. Marga, the Chaplain at Namaste, did a presentation for the Family Support Group in which she pointed out that the grieving that occurs with Alzheimer's is not just about the loss of the person, but the loss of the person we then got to know, then the loss of that one, and the loss of that one.

I could relate. I had gotten a lot of practice with grieving the loss of Ron over the years, so I wasn't paralyzed by it as the end neared. I could simply feel love. I was grateful for that.

Looking at what may have been happening through the lens of our intention to release old patterns when we got married, what was occurring was fascinating. Throughout our Alzheimer's journey, I continued to come up against the limitations that I had placed on myself due to my earlier conditioning. However, I was becoming more confident and authentic, and learning that I had the courage to embrace uncertainty and to trust life. And now, I was seeing that I had even deepened my ability to love. I wondered, what about Ron?

I seemed to be learning to let go and just be. Maybe that was occurring for him, as well, on some level. Since he had Alzheimer's, it would make sense as he didn't seem to have a choice any longer. If he was simply responding to how things felt in the moment, he must have been feeling the love too.

Throughout our relationship, one of the things that Ron struggled with was the feeling that he was not wanted or loved. Having been conceived out of wedlock when his parents were young, as an adult he tried to talk to them about it so he could understand and heal some of his own emotional wounds, but they would never open up. In fact, they avoided the subject at all costs.

It didn't seem unusual for people of that age, at that time. But it was very frustrating to Ron. In his poem entitled "conceived in another time," he wrote –

and when I inquire tell me of my conception
they chastise me with unyielding eyes
why would you want to hear of that!? she says
and he casts a stern look to the floor

Occasionally when the staff was changing Ron and preparing him for his naps, I had a strong sense that he was benefitting deeply in some way. I wondered if the care, acceptance, and love that he was receiving, including the changing of his diaper, may have been healing what was missing for him as an infant, in a similar way that the journey of caring for him had been healing for me. I certainly had become open to possibilities and ways of seeing life beyond those that I had previously been aware of.

What I later read in Megan's book explained what I had surmised. Having observed much while working with individuals with memory impairment, she addressed the possibility that some of the dynamics involved in a person's birth and early years can play out in their journey with memory loss and end-of-life transition.

She says, "What if this is a rich, deeply meaningful period in the person's life and their understanding of their innermost aspect of themselves?"[6] She later points out that perhaps, when faced in life by something that cannot be resolved by their rational side, "the inner conflict results in a need to vacate," so the spirit "becomes vulnerable to demented states of mind."[7] In fact, maybe their essence is experiencing "vistas and possibilities" as a result of the memory loss, that would "defy description" if seen from a logical perspective.[8]

To me, that was a fascinating way to see it. I wondered if that was what was going on with Ron? Maybe having Alzheimer's was a way for him to heal what he carried from his infancy and childhood.

Despite the issues that were apparently involved in both Ron's and my journeys, including the loss and the deep healing that was taking place with each of us; there was also the need to prepare logistically for what was to come, beyond the financial planning. Marga addressed those at the next meeting of the support group when she spoke of the importance of the family being prepared for their loved one's death. I was grateful that Sara attended the meeting with me.

Marga explained that the staff at Namaste was very skilled in identifying when a person had reached the point where their passing was imminent, after which they may go on for a few days or even weeks. She said at that point the staff focuses on keeping the person calm and comfortable. Because of the community orientation and family focus at their facility, they don't isolate the resident but keep them in their normal room. She told of the sensitivity that the other residents often have and explained how one of the residents recently scooted her wheelchair into the room of a woman who was dying and rubbed her feet.

Marga also said that after the person dies, the staff washes their body, and the family is welcome to participate. She explained that this was a way to honor the person and their death. I recalled hearing from Wayne how he did that when Gail passed, and how comforting he found it to be.

Marga further explained that, unlike hospitals, Namaste does not have a morgue so they are limited in the length of time in which they can keep a deceased resident until they need to be picked up by the mortuary. In addition, they did not have a back door through which they take those who have died but take them down the main hall and out the front door, as death is part of the process of life and is not to be hidden.

I had been in the hallway when they were doing that and must say it was a bit uncomfortable. Having worked at the hospital where death was hidden, we were never aware when they were moving a deceased patient from their bed to the morgue and when they were moved them from the morgue to the funeral home, they went through an underground tunnel and out a back door.

After learning about the way death was handled at Namaste, I decided it would be good to advise all of Ron's family of their role and my plans following his death. I had learned about a service called Science Care, where the remains of a deceased person can be sent so that various body parts can be removed for use in science. I felt that Ron, having described studying body parts retrieved from a corpse when he was in dental school, would support that. They are then cremated, and the survivors receive the ashes in the mail a few weeks later. There is no cost to the family for that service, which I had heard about from my friends who had already used it after their spouses passed away. As a result, I told the family that there would be no funeral home or "viewing" involved. I felt they should know that.

When Helen's husband, Bill, passed away, I began to get a stronger sense that Ron's life would be coming to an end before long. Someday he wouldn't be at Namaste, nor anywhere else. After the busyness of the previous year, I began to visit him twice instead of three times a week and started taking more time for myself—cleaning my desk, walking, and journaling. I noticed missing Ron when I wasn't with him but was also noticing my readiness for it to be over. I was puzzled by the conflicting feelings I was having.

One day when I was with Ron, Chris who was his primary daytime caregiver, laid him in his bed after his meal. Ron proceeded to have quite a coughing spell. I held his head next to my body and wondered if he was going to breathe again. Eventually he gasped and took another breath, but I wrote in my journal that I would have been at peace had that not happened. I cried, writing, "My heart aches as I write this. It feels like there is even more distance now." Ron seemed more gone and could no longer respond when I asked him questions or tried to sing with him. I noted that I was exhausted after feeding him, as it felt like it was taking more effort. Maybe that was emotional effort. I struggled.

I wanted to reduce my visits even more to make space so I could rest and become familiar with the emptiness that I would eventually experience, but at the same time, I wanted to be close to Ron and didn't want him to be alone.

Chapter 18

RON'S DECLINE WAS CONTINUOUS, THOUGH slow. He was sleeping more; no longer staying awake very long after eating. In fact, occasionally he was so sleepy when he was sitting at the table for his meal, he couldn't even eat. At times like those, we put him back in bed.

Sometimes he seemed to recognize who I was but couldn't get any words out. His ability to speak was gone.

I noted in my journal that I was looking forward to the coming spring weather so I could take him outside more. When I wrote about how nice it would be for him to sit in the sunshine once again, recalling how much he liked that from the beginning, I began to sob. I seemed to be getting a sense that might never happen again.

After breakfast one day Ron started coughing hard and his face got red until finally, he gasped for air. I had also been noticing when I fed him, that toward the end of his eating he would often cough up a glob of thick mucus. Perhaps that was the result of the medication that the doctor had prescribed for him to help minimize his drooling. At other times, much of his food would just come back out due to his increasing inability to swallow.

Having been aware that the cause of death for the spouses of many friends had been termed "complications of Alzheimer's," I was beginning to wonder if the end would come for Ron as a result of his difficulty in swallowing. Or maybe it would be related to his breathing. Or perhaps both, since they seemed interrelated.

I remembered that his dad passed away due to "aspiration pneumonia," after accidently inhaling some food. It had to come to an end somehow. And having chosen hospice care, we weren't going to do anything about treating the symptoms, nor was that the focus at Namaste. We were just going to keep him comfortable.

In addition to the difficulty with swallowing and breathing, Ron continued to lose weight even when he had been eating well. In fact, he had been losing weight ever since he was accepted by hospice almost two years prior when he was still living at home. That's how he continued to meet the criteria so he was not discharged from their care.

The hospice physician explained to me that, especially as a person in Ron's condition approaches their death, their body expends a lot of energy in just keeping their organs functioning. She said it would be equivalent to the amount of energy and calories a normal person would expend running around the block a few times. In addition to that, Alzheimer's patients are often unable to absorb the nutrients in food as they once did. That was a good description that helped me make sense of it all.

In the meantime, occasionally when I saw Ron, I noticed a bit of blood trickling out of the corner of his mouth or on the cloth that was under his chin to absorb his drooling. The blood did not seem to cause him to cough or interfere with his eating, though.

One day when I was visiting, I brought it to the attention of the staff nurse but she was unable to get Ron to open his mouth so she could look more carefully. It appeared that perhaps he had bitten his tongue.

Around that same time, one evening I received a call from John, who had been a good friend of Ron's when they were working on their counseling degrees in graduate school. He told me that he and his wife had retired and were preparing to move away and said he would like to go see Ron before they leave town.

I updated him on Ron's condition and told him that would probably be the last time he would see him. We made a plan to go together the following week right after the evening meal had been served at Namaste when, hopefully, Ron would still be awake.

Given his condition, Ron just stared at the floor when we first arrived. We pulled up some chairs and sat near him. After our visit, John explained to me that he closed his eyes and with Ron in his heart and mind, silently thanked him for being an important part of his life and acknowledged the contribution they had both made as Licensed Professional Counselors. He then imagined asking Ron to give him a sign if he knew that he was there, after which John opened his eyes. At that point, he said Ron raised his head and looked directly into his eyes with clarity. John said he then knew that Ron recognized him and felt their connection.

He told me later that he knew it was the last time he would see Ron as he hugged him goodbye. Following their time together, he was inspired to write this poem, which he called, "Ron":

> *He stays silent*
> *Deep in his light*
> *Quiet yet aware*
> *In Spirit's presence*
> *His time nigh*
> *The path complete*
> *Eyes that see*
> *My friend with me*
> *~ John McGill*

Reprinted with permission of the author.

That weekend, Sara visited her dad on Saturday, and I visited him on Sunday. We talked later and both mentioned that he seemed more responsive than he had been of late. In fact, when I was there, he even ate his entire pureed lunch. That was a surprise. I left wondering how much longer he would be at Namaste, as there were other residents, also bedridden and needing to be fed, who had been in that state of decline much longer than Ron.

When I later told the doctor about Ron's perkiness when Sara and I saw him that weekend, she said he was probably being his best for us. She said it isn't unusual for someone to do that—even start talking— when they are getting close to death.

The next day, Monday, the hospice nurse called me to say she had been able to get Ron's mouth open and saw some sort of wound on the roof of his mouth that appeared to be bleeding. That was evidently what was causing the blood that I had seen. Since the doctor was scheduled to see Ron the coming Wednesday and I had just seen him the previous day, I decided to wait and go in again on Wednesday when I could discuss it with her.

However, early on Tuesday morning, I received a call from the nursing director at Namaste who said that Ron was in a terminal state. She assured me that it could last for several days or even weeks.

I wanted to go see him, but I hadn't taken a shower yet, so I called Sara to tell her. She was preparing to leave for work, but she said she would go be with her dad until I got there.

Suddenly, though not surprisingly, things were changing.

When I got to Namaste about an hour later, the staff had already moved Ron's roommate to a different room temporarily, so we could have private time with him. We appreciated that. Sara had also called other family members to let them know the condition of her dad.

A few minutes later, Ron coughed up a massive amount of what looked like dark blood. It wasn't bright red, so it appeared to have been accumulating for a while. We assumed he had been swallowing it from the wound on the roof of his mouth prior to his coughing spell. We notified the staff, and they came in and cleaned him up. Ron didn't seem to be in any pain. He was just sleepy. But that was not unusual.

Grandson Dan and his wife had come shortly after receiving Sara's call that morning. Then, during the afternoon more and more family arrived. Granddaughter Beth was able to get someone to watch her little ones so she could come and their brother Jake, who had not been as directly involved in caring for his grandpa, came, as well as Aleah and Moira.

We learned that Tom would be getting into town late that night and Curt was going to let us know when he could get a flight from California.

We congregated in Ron's room and remembered special times with him. We laughed and cried. From time to time one of us would go to his bedside, hold his hand, stroke him, and share something with him.

Later in the afternoon, he coughed up more of the dark blood. It didn't seem like he was vomiting, just coughing. The afternoon staff came in to clean him up and changed his diaper as well. I asked them if there was any evidence of blood in his stool and they said there was not. Apparently, he was not swallowing it.

In a conversation I later had with the hospice physician, she explained how they had been unable to determine the nature of the wound on the roof of Ron's mouth since they couldn't look at it closely or biopsy it. However, she said that due to his difficulty in eating plus the Alzheimer's affecting how his body could assimilate nutrients, it could be that he wasn't getting enough vitamin K to help his blood coagulate. Thus, whatever was on the roof of his mouth was probably bleeding more than normal. Then, when he lay down, she thought the blood was probably pooling in the back of his throat and after substantial accumulation, he coughed it up.

As evening came, we all went to a place nearby where we could get a bite to eat. Dan and Jake stayed on with Ron for a little while and got ahold of Curt on the phone so he and his dad could have face time. After dinner Aleah and I went back to Namaste and my sister, Nancy, stopped by. I was exhausted and was torn about whether to stay overnight with Ron or just go home. The night nurse was older and had clearly seen a lot over the years. She reminded me that Ron could go on for quite some time and suggested I take care of myself. I left with barely enough energy to drive home.

Aleah stayed on for a little while after Nancy and I left. She explained that while she was with Ron, she told him that we all loved him, and it was okay for him to go. She also told him that she would take care of me.

Later that evening, Tom arrived. He said when he got to Namaste, it was really dark and described it as peaceful. He spoke with the nurse on duty then went into his dad's room. He was tired from the drive on top of a long day of teaching and preparing lesson plans. He said it felt good just to sit next to his dad and hold his hand, talking about the times he remembered doing special things together and telling him he loved him. He said Ron opened his eyes off and on and looked at him, but other than that he was still. Tom described it as "a very calm and loving time" and said that after about an hour being with his dad, he left to get some sleep at his mom's.

I awoke early the next morning and went to Namaste. When I went into Ron's room, Marga, in her role of Chaplain, was sitting next to his bed. She told me she was staying with him because his condition changed a bit and he seemed like he could go at any time. She left and I took her place, just being with Ron, holding his hand, and telling him that I loved him. Tom arrived a few minutes later with his guitar. He was thinking he would play some music for his dad.

However, that moment called for quiet, so we shared a few words then sat on either side of Ron, holding his hands and paying close attention to his breathing. It was very labored at that point—his breaths were widely spaced, raspy, and uneven. He didn't seem comfortable, and Tom said, "Dad, if you want to let go, it's okay."

Then Ron took a deep breath with a slow exhalation. We waited patiently and watched for his next breath, but eventually realized that he no longer seemed to be inhaling. We looked at each other and watched. Still nothing. The moment was so calm. Quiet flooded the room. It was over.

As what just happened began to register with us, the quiet was replaced by sounds of the flood of the emotions that Tom and I were experiencing. Our tears flowed, along with sobbing, and even a little giggle due to our surprise at how quickly and easily it all happened.

Ron didn't seem to struggle or try to hang on. We were glad for that—yet he was gone. We sat with him for a few minutes to be with our experience. Then there was a knock on the door.

The staff evidently heard us and asked if we needed them. We told them what happened. They weren't surprised. They had just finished breakfast with the other residents and were cleaning up. Chris told me he would be in shortly to bathe Ron's body with warm water and lavender oil as Marga had explained they would do.

The doctor from hospice later told me that the ultimate cause of Ron's death may very well have been that some of the blood he had been coughing up got into his lungs. She said it would have been very irritating and would likely cause a rapid onset of pneumonia, similar to what occurred with his dad. That could be why he passed away so quickly after the initial symptoms.

In the meantime, Tom began calling his family to let them know and I called Aleah. Sara was the first to arrive and joined us in bathing Ron's body. We worked silently, through our tears. It wasn't so much about cleaning Ron but was more a ritual through which we could love him and acknowledge his passing. We then put lotion on him, after which Chris dressed him in a hospital gown and we covered his body with the colorful comforter that Sara had made for him.

When we opened the door, we discovered others had arrived. Aleah and Jim were there, as well as Ron's grandchildren: Beth, Jake, Caleb, Dan and his wife, Allie.

The head nurse had called the hospice and notified the funeral home, as well. I asked that she request they give us as much time as possible before coming to pick up Ron's body.

Our time with Ron was like the day before, though there were more feelings being expressed as we each grieved. We supported one another. From time to time one of us would stand beside the bed with our head on Ron's body, sobbing. We were going to miss him.

Tom played "This Old Bag of Bones." In recalling that, he said he was a little embarrassed at the choice of songs, but he thought his dad would have appreciated it. Besides, now his spirit was "flyin' free." He said Ron remembered the words to other Guy Clark songs that he sang to him well into his dementia. He had missed the opportunity to play the James Taylor song, "You Can Close Your Eyes," as he was planning to do when he first arrived.

Later, Marga offered a ceremony in which we all surrounded Ron's bed, holding hands. As we gathered, Tom suggested that we take a few deeps breaths together. He said his dad always counseled him to notice his breath to become mindful, drop more fully into the moment, and let go of stress. That was a great way to transition into the ceremony. Then, Marga slowly began holding her hands over each part of Ron's body, while we said together, "You will always be part of our hearts. Go in peace."

That felt healing for all of us and was a very special way to bring our time with Ron to a close.

Shortly after that, we were told that the gentleman from the funeral home had arrived to pick him up. They asked us to leave the room so they could prepare Ron's body for transport, which we did... briefly. Then we went back in. We had been with Ron through the whole thing. They didn't understand. We wanted to be with him as long as we could and did not want to be excluded. We had already seen it all anyway.

As Sara and I had learned earlier, the bodies of those who die at Namaste are taken out through the main hallway so they could be honored. Ron was placed in a body bag on a stretcher, with the quilt that Sara made, covering him. We were all going to walk with him as he was taken to the van for transport to the funeral home. I asked Chris to walk with us, as well. I wanted to include him due to the loving care he provided to Ron and as a result, the comfort we all felt in knowing he was in such good hands. Chris felt like part of the family.

What I didn't know was that the administrative staff would be lining the hallway as we passed through. The tears were rolling down my cheeks. Our journey with Alzheimer's, and Ron's days, including almost two years at Namaste, were over. To top it off when we got outside to the van, the shrine on the mountain above was chiming since it was noon. At the same time a goose on the pond was honking his farewell. What a way for it to end. It couldn't have been better. In fact, those last few minutes seemed to have a celebratory aspect to them. Ron would have loved it. It was weird to talk about him in past tense. He still seemed so "there."

As the van pulled away, we were all stunned. Now what? They told us that we could leave Ron's things in his room overnight, so we didn't have to busy ourselves with that until the next day. We decided to go to my house so we could regroup and get something to eat.

Aleah had called Nancy shortly after learning that Ron died, to let her know what happened. When we arrived, she had arranged an assortment of cold cuts, salads, and snacks that she picked up for us to eat. We really appreciated her thoughtfulness, as we certainly hadn't taken time to eat, and we were hungry.

I learned from the funeral home that I needed to finalize the forms for Science Care, which I did online. Then, as the afternoon wore on, we began to notify others and talk about when and where to have a memorial for Ron. We decided to do it a month later, at an outside venue with which we were all familiar.

After they all left, I collapsed into bed. That had been a big day.

The next morning, I began calling and sending messages to let my friends know that Ron was gone, many of whom were on Facebook.

In the middle of doing that, I was stunned when an ad popped up for a silver necklace with a heart that was inscribed with the words, "I love you, a bushel and a peck." I had not previously been to any site to look at jewelry like that, so how did they know? Then I realized it must have been a gift from Ron. Wow! It was like he was reaching back to let me know of his love and appreciation for my part in the journey we shared.

Curt had gotten into town the previous evening and said that he would like to go to Namaste to remember his dad, thank the staff, and bring healing and closure for himself. He invited us all to join him and that worked for me, as Aleah and I were going there anyway to clean out Ron's things. His children came as well.

Curt asked the staff to join us in Ron's room where he thanked them for the care they gave his dad and offered a prayer. Afterward, he expressed how grateful and blessed he felt to have had that experience after the rest of us had had such a special day before he arrived, caring for Ron, telling him goodbye, and seeing him off. That brought yet another meaningful closure to Ron's time at Namaste.

We all were deeply touched by our experience, and, as Curt said, we had "no regrets." When I contacted the hospice doctor to talk to her, since Ron died the day she was planning to see him, she was amazed and said, "It sounds like it had been scripted" and "was all so perfect." She said it was good that Aleah told Ron that she would take care of me, and that we then left him alone that night so he could "decide" what to do when he was by himself. Then, she said that the morning he passed, he clearly wanted me and Tom with him.

As the days went on, we were all still in touch via email. Beth wrote, "This whole week has been amazing." And Dan responded, saying "It sure has been. I think Papa would love to see us learning and growing so much through this process. What a gift."

Jake shared that through the experience, he saw "the love, under-standing, and companionship that we all fostered for each other," and said, that it "reaffirmed the power of family for me." Jake also said he was touched by the experience, and it helped him realize that a peaceful death can be a wonderful gift. It was hard to imagine how the death of our beloved husband, father and Papa could be so rich and fulfilling.

Ron's niece in California wrote, "We all took comfort in knowing that Uncle Ron was so loved and well taken care of."

And my friend Karen, in hearing about it wrote, "Who would have ever imagined that Ron's process would be such a gift to the family?"

I must say, I agreed with her. Over the years I had come to under-stand the gifts that being with him during his illness had provided for me. Then seeing how it brought the whole family together was truly inspiring.

Chapter 19

IN THE COMING DAYS WE made plans for Ron's memorial service. We knew we wanted it to be about a month after his death, at the outdoor garden venue where several of the kids had gotten married. Ron loved it there. We decided to have it in the late afternoon and began arranging for the caterer and musicians. We met with Marga as we wanted her to lead the service, with others reading poems and sharing memories. Caleb worked on a display with copies of some of Ron's art so the guests could enjoy looking at it. After we chose the date, we notified those in Ron's family who lived out of state.

Ron was not a guy who liked fancy flower arrangements, as he expressed so aptly in the poem he wrote, entitled "memorial day."

the earth will rise up shaking beneath your feet
if you lay cut flowers or set vases from floral shops, or
god forbid! plant miniature tea roses next to my marker
celebrate me in the prairie with strong wind
freshening your hair or if you come, come bearing cattails
or sprigs of nameless beige plants that please your eye
and lay them on my mound until the gusts raise them up
and scatter them on others

That made it easy to choose the decorations. In order to honor his wishes, Aleah and I went to my cousin's ranch to gather "nameless beige plants" and grasses for the arrangements we were going to put on the tables where the guests would be sitting.

One afternoon Aleah and Beth both got off work early and came to the house where they diligently put what we had collected into small vases. For the service, I also decided to do a vase of sunflowers as Ron had grown them in our yard each year, to provide seeds for the birds. That seemed fitting. We certainly weren't going to have a floral shop do the arrangement. The earth was not going to "rise up shaking beneath [our] feet!"

In the interim, while preparing for the service, I was feeling a sense of relief as well as a new layer of sadness. The sadness seemed like it was related to recognizing that with Ron gone, all the love I had been feeling would have nowhere to go. That love had been magnified on the days around Ron's death when the family and I shared those special times together.

I had always been good at *doing*, but the time accompanying Ron on his journey, especially in the end, highlighted the importance of *being*, especially being love with no strings attached. I didn't want that to end.

Thankfully, I still had our cat, Eliot. He had probably been deprived of love over the years with the focus on Ron. For now, I could love him.

The afternoon of the service in late May, was beautiful and warm with the sun dropping lower in the southwest sky as we gathered. In addition to our immediate families there were many friends, members of Ron's poetry group, folks he had known prior to our marriage, and some with whom I had worked, in attendance.

At 5:00 p.m., Marga tapped a small Tibetan bowl to indicate the beginning of the service. The soft sound helped us all pause and gently come into that moment. She went on to say, "We gather in love to honor the life journey of Ron Noel, to remember Ron and his characteristics, to recognize our loss, and to celebrate his transition from this life." She then invited everyone there to take some deep breaths as I had done while I was caring for Ron over the years and as Tom had reminded us to do the day we blessed Ron's body after he died. That would help us all become anchored together in that moment.

Then, she led us in a ritual in which pebbles were put into a bowl to honor the various aspects of Ron and the gifts he gave us. Among the things remembered were his love of nature and the prairie; his creativity and poetry; his struggles to find his authentic self; his wisdom and ability to listen to others; his humility; and the various stages he had gone through in his life—in the end being totally dependent on others to care for him.

At one point in the ceremony, Dan spoke to acknowledge and thank those who had provided care to Papa during the journey. He said that in addition to the day-to-day physical care, other things that had been important during Ron's Alzheimer's journey were the provision of dignity, art, music, love, friendship, and food. In particular, he said he felt like having Alzheimer's magnified Papa's love of burgers, Dr. Pepper, and malts.

That was true. I remembered the day Mike and Gail from the garden shop where Ron had worked, brought a burger and malt from Cy's to have lunch with Ron when he was at Namaste. They knew what he liked.

When acknowledging my role in caring for Papa, Dan said, "Feeding, bathing, and exercising a grown man is no small feat. We know it was a labor of love, but it was definitely laborious, and we all watched in awe as you devised new methods to care for him so that he could remain at home for as long as he did, drenched in your love every day." I guess that was true. Indeed, it was a profound journey for me.

He also talked about watching his dad, Curt, care for his ailing father. He then thanked Steve and Caleb, the others who were Ron's primary caregivers, for their help. In closing, Dan mentioned how he "loathed" the idea of Papa going to a nursing home to die, but then talked about how surprised and impressed he had been with the care he received at Namaste.

Shortly after Dan sat back down next to me, we were nudging each other with our elbows. We had each noticed the shadows of some birds fluttering amongst the foliage on the other side of a shade that had been lowered to keep the sun out of our eyes.

Afterward when we talked, we confirmed that in that moment we were feeling Ron's presence in the birds. Later, we discovered some of the other family members had sensed that as well.

After Dan's sharing, more of Ron's poetry was read by a friend, another friend sang "Keep Me in Your Heart for a While," and an acapella choir of women, The Threshold Singers, sang some additional songs. Then, Marga once again tapped the bowl three times to close the ceremony and invited folks to stay on to share memories and get a bite to eat. The sun was getting low in the sky and beginning to sink over Ron's beloved Cheyenne Mountain by that time.

For those of us who had been involved in caring for Ron and were with him during his dying process, there was one more step in bringing our journey to a close. It would involve the immediate family. We would take his ashes to scatter them on the prairie, "with strong wind freshening [our] hair," but that would come later.

About a week after the service, I found myself feeling really tired. That was the first time I had totally paused after all the busyness, both while caring for Ron at home and visiting him at Namaste, then preparing for his memorial service. Suddenly, it felt like I didn't have anything to do.

I noted the following poem in my journal, as it spoke to me regarding where I was in my own journey.

Clearing

Do not try to save
the whole world
or do anything grandiose.
Instead, create
a clearing
in the dense forest
of your life
and wait there
patiently,
until the song
that is yours alone to sing
falls into your open cupped hands
and you recognize and greet it.
Only then will you know
how to give yourself
to this world
so worthy of rescue.
~ Martha Postlethwaite

Reprinted with permission of the author.

As the days went on, I became clear that my "song" was to some-how support others who were caring for a loved one with Alzheimer's. During the journey, I saw so many struggling as I did in the beginning. Yet, I didn't know exactly what form my support would take, or exactly what the tune would be. Anyway, it wasn't time for those details, yet.

I remembered the lesson I had learned while caring for Ron. When I could get out of the way, stop trying to figure everything out, and not worry about things, I could be more present to what was actually occurring. Then, I could trust the process to show me what to do. The solutions were not so much a result of planning and *doing*, but of *being*. It seemed like practicing that now would "create a clearing" that would allow my life to come together in a new way.

I found myself wishing I could go back and see Ron one more time. It felt like it all happened so suddenly, as it was barely twenty-four hours from the time he entered the terminal state until it was over. I was also remembering how life with Ron had been before Alzheimer's. Interestingly, during most of his disease I never thought much about that part of our lives. I was too focused on what was happening and what I needed to do.

I was surprised that even though I had lived by myself for almost two years while Ron was at Namaste and had managed our lives for a long time before that, I felt somewhat stunned, afraid, and vulnerable. I could see how much easier it was for me to be busy and have a defined role, but thanks to my mindfulness practice, I also knew it was important to pause and simply be with what I was experiencing.

Though I thought I had processed my losses during our journey, the finality of this time made them rawer. I no longer had a career, nor did I have a husband. And now I was not even a care partner. I was just me. I didn't have a clear role to fill. I watched my old beliefs, that I was not worthy or capable, begin to arise. What was I going to do? How was I going to manage?

Phillip Moffitt, spoke of "starting over" which he says involves "shifting your attention away from trying to control the outcome," and "abandoning your usual reactions such as criticizing and judging." He went on to say, doing that "switches your focus away from dwelling on those characteristics that limit you and redirects it toward recognizing your strengths."[1]

I had been learning about my strengths while on the journey with Ron. I now had the opportunity to apply what I learned as I navigated my own life. I could practice starting over in my life as it was now, applying the skills that were helpful and letting go of what was no longer needed, especially the fear and judgment.

I reminded myself how well I had handled caring for Ron, which included buying a new house and moving us, then arranging for him to live at Namaste, and managing all the financial issues. On top of that, people had raved about his memorial service. All that reflected how well I could *DO*, but now it was time for me just to *BE* for a while—sleep in, take walks, have coffee with friends, putter in the garden.

Taking some time out felt right. In honoring that, I could see myself practicing what I had learned about *being love* with Ron, except this time I was directing it to myself.

Since the beginning of the year prior to Ron's death, as his decline was becoming more pronounced, I had begun to prepare for the time when I would be alone. In fact, in January I wrote in my journal that it was time to "start focusing on my own needs and become clearer about the direction I want to go after Ron passes." Then, in stating my intentions for that year, I wrote, "I intend to become more conscious of choices that I make and be willing to honor and support my own well-being." I didn't want to get back into old ruts.

Having heard over and over about the importance of taking care of myself while I was caring for Ron, I began taking better care of my body. I got a referral for physical therapy to resolve an issue with the rotator cuff in my shoulder, so I could have full range of motion. Then, I decided it was time to start exercising, so I registered at a neighborhood gym that recognized the Silver Sneakers program which was a benefit of my health insurance. I found myself crying in class when the song, "Gonna Get Along Without You Now," was among the mix that was used to provide music to accompany our routines.

During the period prior to Ron's death, I had also been reading *Daring Greatly*, by Brené Brown. She spoke of the value of living "wholeheartedly", which she defined as "engaging in our lives from a place of worthiness."[2] It also included, "living a life defined by courage, compassion, and connection."[3] She explained, how she found that "the willingness to be vulnerable emerged as the single clearest value," shared by those who she describes as wholehearted. [4]

I saw that I had gotten good training in being vulnerable while caring for Ron and stretching into new, unfamiliar situations, though I still had some limiting beliefs attached to the worthiness piece. Going on with my life would involve healing the limitations I was still carrying from my past. I was no longer willing to let those stop me as I had done previously.

Maggie also told me about a book that was helpful to her, *Beyond the Good-Girl Jail*. In it, Sandra Felt wrote about the natural pattern of our true self that gradually seeks to emerge and grow more solid as we age. She points out that part of ourselves is often, "ignored, suppressed, and even damaged" when we buy into the "unreasonable expectations of others," in our younger years. Her book focuses on how reclaiming and listening "to your true self will bring you fully alive."[5] That certainly spoke to the journey I was on following Ron's death.

I was clear it was important for me to focus on who I was now and be aware when my old patterns began playing themselves out in unhelpful ways.

I could relate to Felt's way of describing it. She calls our conditioning from our past, "the vortex of rules and roles."[6]

Being with Ron during his Alzheimer's provided a big boost to my process of self-discovery and I wanted to honor that. The opportunity to bring awareness to the limiting beliefs I previously held and release them was one of Ron's gifts to me.

I could see the value of using the intelligence, compassion, and wisdom that I used while caring for Ron, for myself. I even wrote in my journal, "I need to hold that in my heart going forward." As a woman of my generation, taking care of myself had been socialized out of my reality. Looking out for others was always top priority. I could see how the pattern played out throughout my life—stopping myself short of achieving a goal, getting some recognition, or doing something that was important to me. I watched myself trying to make sense of all that and when I dropped into *being* with it, I could feel the importance of paying attention to the sadness and uncertainty that was arising.

As I went through my days, I practiced finding ways of being true to myself—even in old familiar activities. I had always liked having the house clean and orderly, but generally saw that from the perspective of something I *have* to do. After all, it was one of my chores. "What would people think?" But now, when I was by myself, I discovered that anything I did or didn't do was really just for me. I could do the dishes, or not do the dishes. It didn't matter.

Having married young, then having Aleah with me part of the time when I was single before marrying Ron, I had not really had an opportunity to live alone and focus solely on my own needs. Besides, earlier in my life I would not have been able to do it. I was still living out of my conditioning and didn't know there was another way. It was only after my recent experience with Ron that I was able to question all that more deeply and understand that I could let it go.

During the time that I was *being* with and unwinding my own patterns, I also continued to let go of Ron. Curt took two trunks of his family stuff out of the basement. I cleaned out his closet and took the clothes that his sons and his grandsons didn't want to the homeless shelter.

At times, he showed up in different ways. One day when Nancy and I were walking in the park, a bird suddenly flew overhead, and I saw red under its wings. Just like when seeing the shadow of the birds at his memorial service, I sensed Ron's presence. That was confirmed when the next woman we passed commented on seeing the bird and said she had seen red-winged blackbirds when she was in Nebraska. I remembered Ron talking about them being in Nebraska too. When I got home, I looked it up in one of his old bird books. There it was. Now I was the one looking things up in the bird books!

Later that day, when I was searching for something online, I "accidently" came across a song by Willie Nelson entitled, "Just Breathe." He had been one of Ron's favorite singers.

The tears came as I listened. The title was something to which I could relate, as many times when I was stressed while caring for Ron, thanks to my mindfulness practice, I would *just breathe* as a reminder to be present. Then in the song, he sings about giving so much and not taking anything in return, loving each other until we die, and ends with words about meeting on the other side. It felt like Ron could have been singing that to me. When it ended, I was sobbing.

In my journal I noted sometimes feeling sort of "topsy-turvy." It felt like I was in the middle of big things that were happening on many levels in my life.

One morning I woke up after having a dream in which two of my great aunts, who passed years ago, had a male caregiver. It was Ron who was caring for them and it felt like he brought them to me so I could see them again.

During the period following Ron's death while focusing on caring for myself, I also attended a six-day silent meditation retreat in California. I remember sobbing during one of the evening meditations.

Later that summer, I took a trip with Karen. We always enjoyed our time together and it felt especially freeing, in that I no longer had to focus on getting back to see Ron or touching base to see how he was doing while I was gone.

The weekend after we returned was when Ron's family and I were planning to say our final goodbyes to him at the Hugo Wildlife Area that he loved. I divided his ashes into white plastic recycled jars so that those attending could each have some to scatter as they wished. I also tied the containers with some twine and a few "sprigs of nameless beige plants," for decoration.

When the day came, some of us stopped at Ron's favorite prairie café on our way, where he often enjoyed breakfast. Once we arrived at the wildlife area and met the others, we all gathered next to the pond. I passed out the containers with Ron's ashes. We each shared a few words before we left the group and wandered on our own, spreading his ashes as we felt called to do. We were celebrating Ron in the prairie, where the "gusts" would be scattering him amongst the nameless beige plants and the birds that he loved.

It was a huge completion for all of us and a celebration, in a way, as well. An end and a beginning. We would now have a place where we could go to remember and be with Ron/Papa. Some of us even came home "bearing cattails" as they were in season, standing tall on the edge of the pond that day. Though we took a few, many remained there in that beautiful setting with Ron. We left, knowing we had honored him well.

Driving home with the mountains on the horizon, I took a deep breath. No doubt someday I would meet him on the other side. Until then, I still had my life to live and discover anew.

Epilogue

In moving on with my life following Ron's death, I have done my best to balance "doing" with "being." I've tried to process what I learned and incorporate it into my life. Beyond all that I became aware of while I was caring for him and the many changes I made personally, perhaps most importantly, I learned a lot about love.

I was in love with Ron earlier in our marriage. Then, as a result of caring for him during his disease process, I discovered *being love*, which I was experiencing at the time of his death.

My transition following his death included resuming some of the activities that he and I had enjoyed before phasing them out due to Alzheimer's. One of those was attending the philharmonic concerts. About a year after he died, I noticed on the schedule that they were going to be playing a piece with which I was familiar. I got tickets so Aleah and I could attend. It was wonderful to be doing that again.

As we were leaving the symphony hall to walk to her car, I glanced back and saw a gentleman who looked familiar. My mind was racing. How do I know him? Then I remembered. It was Ray, whose wife had been at Namaste and died a few months before Ron. He recognized me too, so he joined us, as his car was in the same area where we were parked.

He said he had season tickets and had gone to the concert by himself. He explained that he was trying to get out and do the things that he enjoyed, after having cared for Mary. That was what I was doing too, after caring for Ron.

In the coming months, Ray invited me to coffee, we had dinner with friends who had also been caring for spouses with Alzheimer's, and we went out to breakfast a couple of times. Though he was older, and his life had been much different than mine, we shared the Alzheimer's journey. We had both retired to care for our spouses. There was certainly no lack of things to talk about.

Yet at that time I was busy with my own life, which included doing The Walk to End Alzheimer's with Aleah and some of the grandchildren. In October, I got a call from Ray asking if I could join him for an upcoming philharmonic concert. I thanked him for inviting me, but declined, telling him it was the weekend of my birthday and I had made plans with the family. Then, a few days later, just before my birthday, the doorbell rang, and I answered to find a florist delivering a beautiful floral arrangement with a sweet card from Ray.

I was very touched and called to thank him. In that conversation he invited me to go to the next concert with him. I accepted the invitation. I could see I would enjoy getting out more regularly, as well as getting to know Ray.

I thought we were just friends. However, as we were walking back to the car after attending that concert, he took my hand. A few weeks later we went to breakfast and on the way home, I remember touching his arm and feeling a tender love for him.

We have been enjoying the companionship of one another for almost five years, now. And, I have discovered that having a man in my life who is cognitively functional, has given me an opportunity to understand more about *being love*. After committing to care for Ron when he had Alzheimer's, I loved him, yet it was up to me to take care of myself, get my needs met, set boundaries, and choose how I responded to the situations that arose.

In reading an article on companionship, I was struck when it spoke to the benefits of being "able to take care of yourself without constant aid from your partner."[1] Ray and I do that.

The article also spoke of being "mindful and respectful of each other's time, privacy, and your partner's need to spend time with other people, and on activities that may not include you." We do that too. Those are some of the things we discussed as we began spending more time together. It also relates to what I learned about making sure I took care of myself while I was caring for Ron.

The importance of being able to "listen to your partner with an open heart and… not get angry when something negative arises," was mentioned in the article as well. Ray and I are improving our skills in this area, which sometimes includes setting boundaries, and always includes talking about it. We didn't have the opportunity to do that when we were caring for Mary and Ron.

The article defined companionship as, "that state of being friends, but it goes deeper than even a friendship. It is a closeness or familiarity… between two people who, for whatever reasons, have truly connected." That describes what I experience in being with Ray.

I am very grateful for his companionship. It has enriched my life in numerous ways and has given me the opportunity to learn more about *being love* and having a courageous heart.

Appendix 1

This diagram illustrates that the stages of decline for a person with Alzheimer's are opposite the developmental stages for infants and toddlers. An "impaired elder" begins their journey with full autonomy and ends with a guardian who has primary responsibility for them. An infant begins with a legal guardian and as they mature into childhood and beyond, they become more autonomous.

Family Involvement with Members

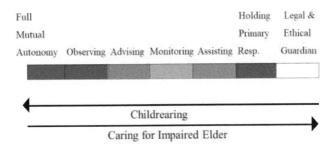

Quaile, 1999

Qualls, S. Honn (1999). Realizing power in intergenerational family hierarchies: Family reorganization when older adults decline. In M. Duffy (Ed.), *Handbook of Counseling and Psychotherapy with Older Adults* (pp. 228-241). New York: J. Wiley & Sons.

Appendix 2

Paying for Care

In general, when professional long-term care is provided either in the home or in a facility, it is paid in one of the following ways (or a combination thereof):

1. Private pay, using the assets of the person receiving the care, and/or family's income and assets.
2. Using a Long Term Care insurance policy, if the person receiving the care has such a policy.
3. Using Medicaid Long Term Care.

It is important to understand that Medicare does not cover long term care, either in the home or in a facility.

Medicaid is not Medicaid is not Medicaid. There are different adult Medicaid programs (waivers) and each one has different financial qualifications. Just because a person qualifies for one adult Medicaid program does not mean they will qualify for every adult Medicaid program. The

Medicaid Long Term Care program (waiver) can be the safety net for the services your loved one may need, but this varies by state.

The Area Agency on Aging should be able to help with learning about the availability of financial programs in your area, thus providing assistance and support to the family care provider with regard to the financial aspects of care. If not, they may know of local resources where the caregiver can get such help, working with the specific financial situation of the patient and their family. The Agency in your area can be found on the following website:

http://www.n4a.org

Clarification provided by Kent Mathews, MSW
Lead Care Manager, Family Caregiver Support Center, Pikes
Peak Area Council of Governments,
Area Agency on Aging

The sites below are also helpful in dealing with financial issues involved in Alzheimer's care.

Centers for Medicare and Medicaid Services:

https://www.cms.gov/
https://www.medicare.gov/
https://www.medicaid.gov/

Social Security Disability Benefits:

https://www.ssa.gov/benefits/disability/
https://www.ssa.gov/compassionateallowances/

Veteran benefits: Like Medicaid Long Term Care, there at a lot of different factors that go into a veteran qualifying for a program to pay for services at a care facility. The Veteran Service Organization can explain all of that to the vet or family member.

The specific State Programs available to assist with programs for veterans can be found at:

https://nvf.org/veteran-service-officers/

Notes

Chapter 4

1. Kabat-Zinn, Jon, Ph.D. *Full Catastrophe Living.* New York: Bantam Doubleday, Dell Publishing Group, Inc., 1990. p. 254.
2. Alzheimer's Association: https://www.alz.org/alzheimers-dementia/10_signs)

Chapter 5

1. Moffitt, Phillip. Facebook, 11/26/2018.
2. Smalley, Susan L., Ph.D. and Winston, Diana. *Fully Present: The Science, Art, and Practice of Mindfulness.* Da Capo Press, 2010. p. 11.
3. Ibid, p. 11.
4. Kabat-Zinn, Jon, Ph.D. *Full Catastrophe Living.* New York: Bantam Doubleday, Dell Publishing Group, Inc., 1990, p. 264.
5. Ibid, p. 250.
6. Ibid, p. 264.
7. Ibid, p. 237.

8. Petro, Steven. *The Washington Post*: "Resilience isn't just being tough; it's a skill you can develop. Here's how I did it". Interview with Tara Brach. 8/29/2017.

Chapter 6

1. Kabat-Zinn, Jon, Ph.D. *Wherever You Go There You Are*. New York: Hyperion, 1994. p. 30.
2. Petro, Steven. The Washington Post: "Resilience isn't just being tough; it's a skill you can develop. Here's how I did it". Interview with Tara Brach. 8/29/2017.
3. Hauck, Carley. https://www.mindful.org/how-people-learn-to-increase-their-resilience/ 3/3/2016.
4. Kabat-Zinn, Jon, Ph.D. *Full Catastrophe Living*. New York: Bantam Doubleday, Dell Publishing Group, Inc., 1990. p. 251.
5. Qualls, Sara Hon, Ph.D. *Caregiving: How do you know when it is time?* Alzheimer's Association, workshop. April 2013.

Chapter 7

1. The Alzheimer's Association: https://www.alz.org/help-support/caregiving/daily-care/incontinence
2. Neff, Kristin, Ph.D. Self-Compassion: https://self-compassion.org/the-three-elements-of-self-compassion-2/
3. Ibid, Neff, Kristin
4. Ibid, Neff, Kristin
5. Armstrong, Sally. Transforming Suffering: The Resilience of a Compassionate Heart. https://www.spiritrock.org/the-teachings/article-archive/dukkha-sally-armstrong
6. Ibid. Armstrong, Sally
7. Graham, Linda, MFT. Mindfulness, Self-Compassion and Resilience. https://learning.hccs.edu/faculty/peggy.porter/authentic-voices/mindfulness-self-compassion-and-resilience, 2016.

Chapter 11

1. Tull, Deborah Eden. *Relational Mindfulness.* Wisdom Publications, 2018. p. 51

Chapter 12

1. allnurses. https://allnurses.com/what-are-phases-alzheimers-disease-t12848/, 2002.

Chapter 13

1. Rick Hanson. "Just One Thing" Newsletter. https://www.rickhanson.net/nourish-yourself/
2. Alzheimer's Association. https://www.alz.org/help-support/caregiving/stages- behaviors/late-stage.

Chapter 15

1. The Dementia Queen. The 5 Most Common Problems in Late Stage Alzheimer's Disease. http://thedementiaqueen.com/2012/01/the-5-most-preventable-problems-in-late-stage-alzheimers-disease/. 2012.
2. Ibid. The Dementia Queen.

Chapter 16

1. Family Caregiver Alliance. Caregiver Health: A Population at Risk. https://www.caregiver.org/resource/caregiver-health/?via=caregiver-resources,caring-for-yourself,health.
2. Mindful Magazine. *The Scary Winding Road through Change.* October, 2014. p. 74

Chapter 17

1. Manteau-Rao, Marguerite, LCSW. *Caring for a Loved One with Dementia.* New Harbinger Publications, Inc., 2016. p. 187.

2. Moffitt, Phillip. *Awakening Through the Nine Bodies.* Berkeley, California: North Atlantic Books, 2017. p. 61
3. Ibid, p. 16
4. Ibid, p. 178
5. Carnarius, Megan, RN, NHA, LMT. *A Deeper Perspective on Alzheimer's and Other Dementias.* Scotland, UK: Findhorn Press, 2015. p. 136.
6. Ibid, p. 101
7. Ibid, p. 118
8. Ibid, p. 101

Chapter 19

1. Moffitt, Phillip. Starting Over. https://dharmawisdom.org/starting-over/
2. Brown, Brene, Ph.D., LMSW. *Daring Greatly.* New York: Penguin Random House, 2012. p. 10
3. Ibid, p. 11
4. Ibid, p. 11
5. Felt, Sandra, LCSW. *Beyond the Good Girl Jail.* Deerfield Beach, FL: Health Communications, Inc., 2016. p. 41
6. Ibid, p. 160

Epilogue

1. Irene Valenti. Valenti Matchmaking https://www.valenti-matchmaking.com/2015/03/02/10-tips-perfect-companionship-companionship-vs-relationship/

Resources

Books

Mindfulness:

Chödrön, Pema. *When Things Fall Apart: Heart Advise for Difficult Times.* Shambhala Publications, 1997.

Chödrön, Pema. *The Places that Scare You: A Guide to Fearlessness in Difficult Times.* Shambhala Publications, 2001.

Coleman, Mark, MA. *From Suffering to Peace: The True Promise of Mindfulness.* New World Library, 2019.

Graham, Linda, MFT. *Bouncing Back: Rewiring Your Brain for Maximum Resilience and Well-Being.* New World Library, 2013.

Hanson, Rick, Ph.D. *Just One Thing: Developing a Buddha Brain One Simple Practice at a Time.* New Harbinger Publications, 2011.

Kabat-Zinn, Jon, Ph.D. *Full Catastrophe Living: Using the Wisdom of Your Body and Mind to Face Stress, Pain, and Illness.* Bantam Dell Publishing Group, Inc., 1990.

Kabat-Zinn, Jon, Ph.D. *Wherever You Go There You Are: Mindfulness Meditation in Everyday Life.* Hyperion, 1994.

Moffitt, Phillip. *Dancing with Life: Buddhist Insights for Finding Meaning and Joy in the Face Of Suffering.* Rodale, 2012.

Neff, Kristin, Ph.D. *Self-Compassion: The Proven Power of Being Kind to Yourself.* HarperCollins, 2011.

Salzberg, Sharon. *Loving-Kindness: The Revolutionary Art of Happiness.* Shambhala Publications, 1995.

Smalley, Susan L., Ph.D. and Winston, Diana. *Fully Present: The Science, Art, and Practice of Mindfulness.* Da Capo Press, 2010.

Stahl, Bob, Ph.D. and Goldstein, Elisha, Ph.D. *A Mindfulness-Based Stress Reduction Workbook.* New Harbinger Publications, Inc., 2010.

Tull, Deborah Eden. *Relational Mindfulness: A Handbook for Deepening Our Connection with Ourselves, Each Other, and the Planet.* Wisdom Publications, 2018.

Alzheimer's:

(These are just a few of the many books on Alzheimer's, depending on your interest.)

Carnarius, Megan, RN, NHA, LMT. A Deeper Perspective on Alzheimer's and Other Dementias. Findhorn Press, 2015.

Cohn, Barbra. Calmer Waters: The Caregiver's Journey Through Alzheimer's and Dementia. Blue River Press. 2016

Hoblitzelle, Olivia Ames. Ten Thousand Joys and Ten Thousand Sorrows: A Couple's Journey Through Alzheimer's. Penguin Group, 2008.

Mace, Nancy L., M.A. and Rabins, Peter, M.D., MPH. The 36-Hour Day: A Family Guide to Caring for Persons with Alzheimer's Disease, Other Dementias, and Memory Loss, 6th Edition. Johns Hopkins University Press, 2017.

Manteau-Rao, Marguerite, LCSW. Caring for a Loved One with Dementia: A Mindfulness-Based Guide for Reducing Stress and Making the Best of Your Journey Together. New Harbinger Publications, Inc., 2016.

Other:

Brown, Brene, Ph.D., LMSW. *Daring Greatly: How the Courage to Be Vulnerable T*ransforms The Way we Live, Love, Parent, and Lead. Penguin Random House, 2012.

Felt, Sandra, LCSW. *Beyond the Good-Girl Jail: When You Dare to Live from Your True Self.* Health Communications, Inc., 2016.

Websites

Mindfulness:

Mindful Communications
http://www.mindfulness.org
Much free information from articles to meditations. Also, a seasonal
magazine available by subscription.

Center for Mindfulness in Medicine, Health Care and Society
http://www.umassmed.edu/cfm
Articles, meditations, and classes about Mindfulness-Based Stress
Reduction (MBSR)

UCLA Mindful Awareness Research Center
http://www.uclahealth.org/marc
Articles, meditations, and classes

Support for Alzheimer's Caregivers:

Alzheimer's Association
http://www.alz.org
Invaluable resource for information, help and support including local
chapter contacts

Family Caregiver Alliance
http://www.caregiver.org
Information, resources, and services available by state.

National Association of Area Agencies on Aging
http://www.n4a.org
Excellent site where resources can be found that pertain your local
community including caregiver support and financial assistance.

National Institute on Aging
https://www.nia.nih.gov/health/alzheimers
A wealth of information and education related to Alzheimer's disease,
including resources for care.

Presence Care Project
http://www.presencecareproject.com/
Much free information about Mindfulness-Based Dementia Care
including Resources, Podcasts, Meditations, Videos, etc.

Teepa Snow
http://www.teepasnow.com
Training for Alzheimer's care providers, both personal and professional, on the Positive Approach to Care (PAC). Valuable information,
including videos which are available on YouTube (See info on website
Resources page).

Acknowledgements

This book has come into being with the support of many who were there for me during the various stages of my journey, as an Alzheimer's caregiver, a facilitator of mindfulness, then eventually as an author. I am extremely grateful to GracePoint Publishing for their support in publishing this memoir, so my story could be shared with others whose lives have been affected by Alzheimer's disease.

I would first like to acknowledge my friends Jeanne Katz, Teryl Lundquist, and Steve Milligan, whose support was invaluable though they have now passed away. They were there for conversations to help me come to terms with what was happening and how my life was changing, as well as to support me in self-care by inviting me to join them for such things as lunch, local events, or a trip to the hot springs. I miss them all and regret that they are no longer a part of my life.

Dr. Crandall, the psychiatrist from whom Ron initially sought guidance in trying to understand his dementia, has passed away as well. She played an important role in helping both of us understand what was happening and what lay ahead.

I extend much gratitude to those at the local Alzheimer's Association, whose support in learning to be a caregiver was invaluable. That includes the classes offered by Barbara Caudle, and the support group facilitated by Mary Anne Cooper and Dick Dailey, as well as the information provided by the entire organization.

Kent Mathews, associated with the local Area Agency on Aging, provided much information in helping me become familiar with my new role and directing me to numerous supportive services in the community. The Aging Center at the University of Colorado at Colorado Springs (UCCS) also contributed their expertise as they provided testing of Ron and support for me early on in our journey.

A big thanks to Steve Eustice, Moira Noel, and all the family members who were involved in caring for Ron with hands-on help. It took a major re-set for Caleb Noel to be the one to care for his grandpa instead of the other way around, and the love and skill with which he did that were impressive.

I am very appreciative of Bonnie Bee, who opened her heart at the North End Day Care Center and did a masterful job of "creating community" amongst the caregivers as well as our loved ones. Voyages, a day care program associated with Goodwill Industries, was helpful in caring for Ron, as well.

Many thanks to all who were there for us, primarily during the period when I was caring for Ron at home. Our physician, Mark Fraley, D.O.; friends John McGill, Bob McAtee, Clark Smith, and Mike and Gail Estes; as well as others from Ron's poetry group and art community, offered their support in numerous ways.

Then there were those also caring for their spouse with Alzheimer's, whose support and comradery was invaluable. Some of those folks have continued to be an important part of my life including Ray Alvarado, Duane Carter, Maria Daniels, Ginny Hatton, Dave Kent, Larry Patzer, and Norma Robinson.

When Ron lived at Namaste (CHI Living Communities), his primary caregiver, Chris Forbes, was exceptional in providing loving and patient care of Ron. The services offered by Tabitha Wiseman, the social worker, as well as the support provided by Marga Callender, the chaplain, were also of great value to our family. In fact, the entire staff at Namaste showed a tireless commitment to providing quality care for Alzheimer's patients.

In addition, the staff at Pikes Peak Hospice added their expertise to Ron's care during that time.

Earlier, while Ron was in day-care, my friend Nan Karsh, partnered with me in developing and teaching mindfulness classes for other Alzheimer's caregivers in the community.

I then attended the Mindfulness Certification Program at the Semel Institute, UCLA. The classes provided by Diana Winston, Director, and Marvin Belzer, Associate Director, deepened my understanding of mindfulness and provided valuable support and training, as did the teachings of many others. I was also inspired by the work and friendship of those who were in the program with me, and appreciate the kindness and hospitality offered by Marjorie Pearson, when I was in LA.

The mindfulness retreats that I attended during my respite breaks provided much support as well, thanks to the teachings offered by Bob Stahl, Mark Coleman, Anna Douglas, Brian Lesage, Deborah Eden Tull, and others.

Ultimately, I appreciate Jon Kabat-Zinn for developing the Mindfulness-Based Stress Reduction program, and for his commitment to sharing it with the world. I have been deeply touched and supported by my practice as a result of his vision.

As I became interested in writing a book, I reached out to several who contributed to my skills and understanding in this endeavor. Those primarily include Hay House Publishing, Kathryn Eastburn, and Marion Roach Smith.

I also thank the many friends and family with whom I consulted for their feedback, memories, and review as I was writing. I especially want to express my gratitude to friends Marga Callender and Karen Waters for their time in editing and providing feedback on my draft.

Of great importance in the process of writing *Courageous Hearts*, has been the support and coordination of GracePoint Publishing. Special thanks to Michelle Vandepas, Mark Packard, Tascha Yoder, and many on their staff who were responsible for the editing, coaching, cover design, and publicity. Thanks also to Tanisha Martin, who has provided her skill and knowledge in enhancing my website and supporting me with the publicity.

When I think back on my journey, several of my friends stand out. Maggie Barber listened, shared ideas, and was always generous with her time, as was Karen Latvala. She and her husband, Lyle, also welcomed me to their home so I could take a break and get out of town. And Leeza Steindorf was instrumental in helping me tell my story and get it published, as well as organizing trips to meet up at the hot springs. I cherish my continued relationship with each of these women.

And last but not least, I want to acknowledge our families. They have supported me throughout the processes of caring, grieving, and writing with hands on help, listening ears, suggestions, overnight stays, distractions, meals, you name it. They are introduced in the manuscript when they appear in the journey, but I want to acknowledge them individually here. Ron's family includes his children, Curt Noel, Tom Noel, and Sara Noel, and his grandchildren, Bethany Essendrop, Dan Noel, Jake Noel, and Caleb Noel. Thankfully, they are still an important part of my life. Though Ron's brothers Max Noel and Rick Noel live elsewhere, they were there with support for all of us primarily via email and telephone calls.

A big thanks to my daughter Aleah Karsh and her husband Jim Steinke for their generosity, kindness, and love. They were always willing to pitch in and help me, often at times of an urgent need. And my son, Blaine Fields, encouraged and supported me from a distance with emails and telephone calls. He was also generous with his time and assistance when I was in LA for my coursework.

Then there are those who have been part of my life longer than any of the others – my brother, Jim Arndt and my sister, Nancy Engle. A big thanks to both of them. Though not as directly involved in helping with Ron, I was able to count on their support as I navigated the many unfamiliar experiences in being a caregiver and writing this book. And Nancy, who lives locally, stepped up occasionally when she saw a way that she could assist. I am extremely grateful that the three of us have had a strong life-long bond and continue to be there for one another.

In looking back at this period with the many steps and mis-steps from which I have learned and grown, I have a developed a deep reverence for life itself, and for all with whom I share this journey. For that, I am very grateful.

About the Author

Cyndy Noel has drawn on many of her life experiences in sharing about the journey she had with her husband who had Alzheimer's. Prior to retiring to care for him, she worked at a local hospital as a Patient Representative, supporting patients and their families who were having a difficult time navigating the health care system. As a result, she brings a wide-ranging perspective on what people go through when facing difficult health-related challenges.

Throughout much of her adult life, Cyndy has recognized that there are numerous ways to perceive the situations we encounter. After being introduced to the Mindfulness-Based Stress Reduction Program developed by Jon Kabat-Zinn, she understood that more clearly. Caring for her husband during their Alzheimer's journey gave her many opportunities to put that to the test. She experienced the value of mindfulness as it helped her see the challenges and uncertainty from a different perspective. She then began teaching mindfulness to others who were caring for a loved one and went on to develop classes in mindful aging.

In addition to her Master's in Counseling and Human Services from the University of Colorado in Colorado Springs, Cyndy attended the Semel Institute at UCLA where she became certified as a mindfulness facilitator. She is committed to a daily meditation practice, and occasionally meditates with local groups, either live or on-line. She also participates in silent meditation retreats lasting for up to a week.

Though *Courageous Hearts* is her first book, writing has always been of interest to Cyndy. She has written articles for numerous publications and was involved in publishing a newsletter for parents when her daughter was young.

Cyndy has lived in Colorado most of her life, so having a mountain in sight gives her a strong sense of home. As an elder with some disabilities, she can no longer enjoy the hikes and bike rides that were once an important part of her life, though she still enjoys walking and exercising as ways to stay fit. Time spent with her immediate family and stepfamily, is important to her. Cyndy is also grateful for the many friends she met through her Alzheimer's journey, as well as the friendships she has maintained from earlier in her life.

She enjoys reading, writing, playing Scrabble, gardening, taking walks, and cooking as well as visiting some of the hot springs in Colorado. Whatever the activity, she cherishes the ability to be present and have compassion for herself and others, thanks to her mindfulness practice.

For more great books visit Empower Press online at
Books.GracePointPublishing.com

If you enjoyed reading Courageous Hearts and purchased it through
an online retailer, please return to the site and write a review to help
others find this book.

Lightning Source UK Ltd.
Milton Keynes UK
UKHW011232040922
408313UK00001B/78